Introduction to Our KS4 Workbooks

The central aim of Coordination Group Publications is to produce
top quality teaching and learning material which is carefully
matched to the National Curriculum, and then supply it to schools
and individuals as cheaply as possible.

These brilliant KS4 Science Workbooks have *Three Top Features*:

Carefully Matched to the KS4 Programme of Study

They accompany our Revision Guides which cover every topic
in the National Curriculum. The questions provide perfect
practice material at any stage, but will be especially useful as
preparation for the dreaded GCSEs.

Emphasis on Learning the Basic Facts

Throughout these books there is a constant emphasis on the inescapable need
to *keep learning the basic facts*. This simple message is hammered home
without compromise and without remorse. Whilst this traditionally brutal
philosophy may not be quite in line with some other approaches to education,
we still rather like it. But only because it works.

They're Top Dollar Value

You can buy a set of our workbooks for far less than it would cost to
photocopy an equivalent number of worksheets — and that's not counting
the valuable hours you'd have to spend crouched over a hot photocopier!

That's Top Dollar Value alright!

Buy our books — they're ace

Useful bits for reference

Processes

Diffusion is the movement of particles from an area of ***high*** concentration to an area of ***low*** concentration.

Transpiration is the process by which ***water*** evaporates from the leaf of a plant and causes a column of water to ***rise up the plant*** from the roots.

Photosynthesis produces ***glucose*** and ***oxygen*** from ***carbon dioxide*** and ***water***, using ***sunlight*** and ***chlorophyll***.

Respiration is the process of ***transferring energy*** from ***food*** molecules that takes place in all ***animal*** and ***plant cells***.

Digestion is the process by which food is ***broken down*** into particles small enough to diffuse into the blood.

Homeostasis is the maintenance of a ***constant internal environment***.

Substances

An ***enzyme*** is a ***protein*** that acts as a biological ***catalyst***.

A ***catalyst*** is a substance that ***speeds up*** a chemical reaction ***without being used up*** itself.

A ***hormone*** is a ***chemical message*** that controls biological processes in an organism. In humans, hormones are secreted by ***endocrine glands*** directly into the blood and ***carried in the blood*** to the target organ.

Auxins are hormones produced by ***plants*** that govern the growth of plant shoots and roots.

Genetics

DNA is the molecule which contains ***genes***. It is shaped like a spiral.

Chromosomes are the X-shaped things found in the cell nucleus. The arms are made of ***very long coils of DNA*** , so chromosomes also contain genes.

A ***gene*** is a length of DNA. Each separate gene is a particular chemical ***instruction*** to a certain type of cell.

An ***allele*** is another name for a gene. When you have two different versions of the same gene, you call them alleles instead of genes.

Things not to get confused one with t'other

xylem and ***phloem***	***aerobic*** and ***anaerobic*** respiration
respiration and ***breathing***	***genetic*** and ***environmental*** variation
bacteria and ***viruses***	***glycogen*** and ***glucagon***
sexual and ***asexual*** reproduction	the ***greenhouse effect*** and the hole in the ***ozone layer***.

Contents

Published by Coordination Group Publications
Typesetting and layout by The Science Coordination Group
Illustrations by: Sandy Gardner, e-mail: illustrations@sandygardner.co.uk,
                      Bowser (Colorado USA), Ashley Tyson and Lex Ward.

Coordinated by Paddy Gannon BSc MA

Contributors
Nigel Saunders
Chris Christofi

Design editor: Paul Thompson BSc (Hons)

ISBN 1 84146 619 0

Printed by Hindson Print, Newcastle upon Tyne.
0699

Questions on Biology Apparatus

Q1   *Drawn below are eight pieces of apparatus commonly used in the laboratory.*

Fill in the name for each piece of apparatus and *describe* briefly what it is used for.

Name ....

Used for ....

....

....

....

Name ....

Used for ....

....

....

....

Name ....

Used for ....

....

....

....

Name ....

Used for ....

....

....

....

Name ....

Used for ....

....

....

....

Name ....

Used for ....

....

....

....

Name ....

Used for ....

....

....

....

Name ....

Used for ....

....

....

....

Questions on Biology Apparatus

Q2 In this question, match each piece of apparatus to its correct use (function).

Apparatus ⟹ Function

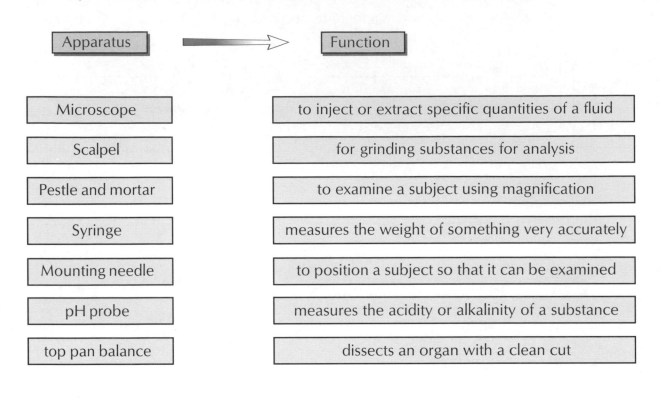

Apparatus	Function
Microscope	to inject or extract specific quantities of a fluid
Scalpel	for grinding substances for analysis
Pestle and mortar	to examine a subject using magnification
Syringe	measures the weight of something very accurately
Mounting needle	to position a subject so that it can be examined
pH probe	measures the acidity or alkalinity of a substance
top pan balance	dissects an organ with a clean cut

Q3 *It is important to choose the correct apparatus for the job. For example measuring a certain volume of liquid in different situations might require a different degree of precision and therefore different apparatus.*

Look at the following situations and choose the most appropriate piece of apparatus from those shown for measuring the desired quantities. Write the correct *letter* in each of the white boxes:

a) 8cm^3 of hydrochloric acid for use in titration.

b) 30cm^3 of water to a fair degree of accuracy.

c) 200cm^3 of water for diluting an acid

to a desired concentration.

d) 200cm^3 of water which will go in a water bath.

e) 25cm^3 of sodium hydroxide for using in titration.

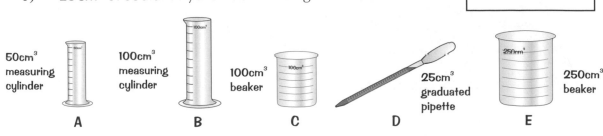

50cm^3 measuring cylinder	100cm^3 measuring cylinder	100cm^3 beaker	25cm^3 graduated pipette	250cm^3 beaker
A	B	C	D	E

Questions on Biology Apparatus

Q4 Match up each *action* with the *correct safety rule* by drawing between them in the diagram below:

| Action | $\longrightarrow$ | Safety Rule |

Action	Safety Rule
Entry into a laboratory	Do not interfere with mains circuit or touch switches with wet hands
Use of apparatus	Wear eye protection, check that the named substance is exactly what you want
Assembly of apparatus	Do not enter any room without permission
Use of chemicals	Touch only when instructed to do so, and use things only for their intended purpose
Electricity	Never push or pull glass tubing into or out of a cork or a bung

Q5 *The following paragraph describes an experiment. Unfortunately the wrong names have been used for a number of pieces of apparatus. These names have been underlined.*

I measured out 250cm³ of water using a *measuring jug* and poured it into a glass bowl. Using a *heater* and a *triangular stand*, I then heated the water. When it reached 100°C on the *thermostat*, I added a *spoon* full of the brown powder and stirred it with a glass *staff*. Using an electronic *weighing scale*, I weighed out 2.5g of white powder and added it the solution. Then with a *100cm³ jug*, I accurately measured out 8cm³ of the white liquid and again added it to the solution.

Decide the correct term for each piece of apparatus, and write it next to the names below:

measuring jug ....   spoon ....

heater ....   staff ....

triangular stand ....   weighing scale ....

thermostat ....   100cm³ jug ....

SECTION ONE — BASIC SKILLS

Questions on Hazards and Safety

Q1   *The picture below shows 15 safety hazards in a school laboratory.*

Identify any 10 out of the 15 safety hazards and list them in the table below.

	Safety Hazards
1	
2	
3	
4	
5	
6	
7	
8	
9	
10	

Questions on Hazards and Safety

Q2 *Below are a number of statements about laboratory procedures.*
Study each statement and decide whether it is a <u>*good*</u> or a <u>*bad*</u> idea, then tick the corresponding box below.

Good idea   Bad idea

☐   ☐   Place all waste material in a waste paper bin

☐   ☐   Never put solids, especially broken glass, in sinks

☐   ☐   Don't bother the teacher over minor cuts and burns

☐   ☐   Always leave an unattended Bunsen on a yellow flame

☐   ☐   Be careful with clothing and long hair near a Bunsen flame

☐   ☐   When heating solids or liquids watch the mouth of the tube carefully

☐   ☐   It is safe to taste very small particles or droplets

☐   ☐   If you take a chemical into your mouth just swallow it

☐   ☐   If you get acid or alkali on your skin or clothing, wash it off with hot water

☐   ☐   Chemicals spilled on the bench should be washed away immediately with cold water and the area wiped clean

☐   ☐   Put waste paper in a bin

☐   ☐   Always add concentrated acids to water — not the other way round

☐   ☐   All reactions that produce gases should be carried out in a fume cupboard

☐   ☐   Always make sure you know where fire extinguishers are located in the lab

Questions on the Microscope

Q1   Much of the living world is too small for human eyes to see — our eyes can only see objects larger than 0.1mm. The microscope is an instrument used for viewing objects normally too small for us to see. The first simple microscope had only one lens but the one generally used today is called a <u>Compound Microscope</u> because it has a series of lenses.

The diagram below shows a compound microscope and its different parts.

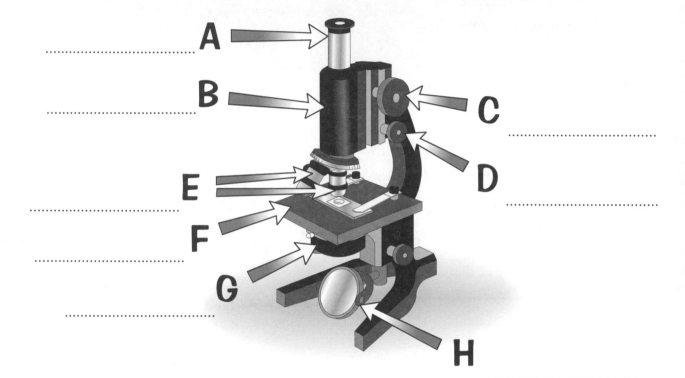

.... **A**

.... **B**

C ....

D ....

.... **E**

.... **F**

G

H ....

a) Complete the labels in the diagram above.

b) Fill in the table below to describe the function of each of the parts in the diagram.

Label	Function
A	
B	
C	
D	
E	
F	
G	
H	

Questions on the Microscope

Q2 Use the words in the box to complete the passage below on the use of the microscope (there are more words than you need).

| mirror | direct sunlight | dry | towards | eyepiece | wipe | high |
| power | objective | slide | low power | objective | | away from |

View any object through the .... and adjust the

.... to obtain maximum brightness. Do not use

.... as this could damage your eyes.

Keep the stage clean and .... and always ....

the underside of the slide. Begin your viewing with the

.... lens, and always move it ....

the object when focusing, to avoid breaking the ....

Q3 *The total magnification of an object is the number of times the item has been enlarged from its actual size. This can be calculated by multiplying the eyepiece magnification by the objective lens magnification. The eyepiece always magnifies things by 10 times — this is expressed as "x10". The objective lens magnification is often x5, x10 or x20.*

For example,   (eyepiece lens) x (objective lens) = (total magnification)
                        x10   x   x10   =   x100

Complete the missing spaces in the table below, assuming that the eyepiece always magnifies by a factor of 10.

Eyepiece	Objective	Total magnification
x10	x5	
	x30	
x10		200
	x10	

Questions on the Microscope

Q4 *When looking down a microscope a clear circle is seen. This is called the <u>Field of View</u>.*

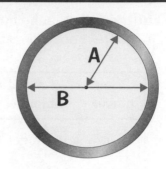

a) *The diagram on the right shows the field of view with two lines, marked <u>A</u> and <u>B</u>.*

Which of these lines is the diameter of the

field of view? ....

To find how big something really is when viewed using a microscope we must know the <u>field of view diameter</u> and how many times our object will fit into it.

If the field of view diameter on low power = 4mm, then Animal 'A' length is exactly the field of view length.

Therefore: $\dfrac{\text{field of view}}{\text{number of animal lengths}} = \dfrac{4mm}{1} = 4mm$

b) *Two more field of view diagrams are shown below. In each case the field of view diameter was 4mm. Calculate the length of each animal by filling in the spaces below.*

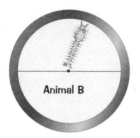

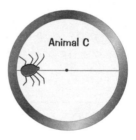

Field of view width = ... mm   Field of view width = ... mm

Number of animal lengths = ...   Number of animal lengths = ...

So length of animal B = ... mm   So length of animal C = ... mm

c) *The specimen below was looked at under the high power lens of a microscope with a field of view diameter of 1mm.*

Calculate the length of object by filling in the spaces below:

Field of view width = ... mm

Number of object lengths = ...

So length of object X = ... mm

SECTION ONE — BASIC SKILLS

Questions on Data Collection

Q1 *John's beehive has lots of bees in it (see the diagram on the right below).*

a) How many bees are there in the hive? ....

If there were hundreds (or thousands) of bees in John's beehive, it wouldn't be possible to count them all one by one.

However, the total number can be estimated by dividing the hive into squares (as shown in the diagram), counting the number of bees in a few of the squares and then multiplying up.

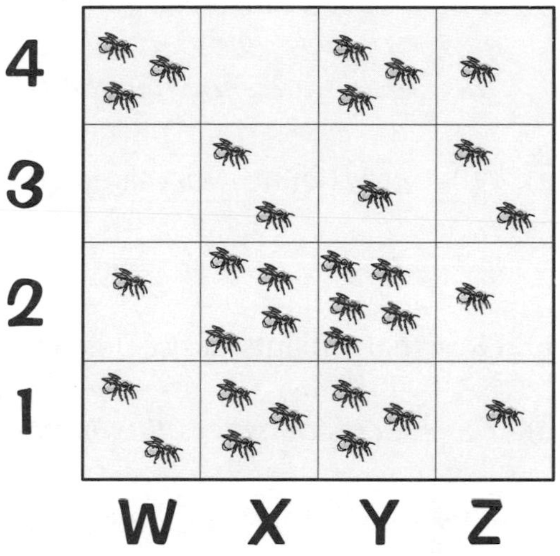

4

3

2

1

W X Y Z

b) How many bees are there in square W1?

....

c) Multiply this number by the total number of squares to get an estimate of the total number

of bees. How close is your answer to the true number? ....

d) Repeat what you did for parts b) and c) for each of the squares Y2 and Z4 individually.

What do you notice? ....

....

e) *The four squares W1, W2, X1 and X2 are combined to form a new, larger, square. This*

square covers one quarter of the total area of the beehive.

i) What is the total number of bees in the new square? ....

....

ii) Multiply the number of bees found in the new square by 4, to get a *new estimate* for the

total number of bees in the hive. How does this answer compare to the actual total?

....

f) What do your answers to d) and e) tell you about the benefit of increasing the sampling

area when estimating the total number of bees present in the hive? ....

....

Questions on Data Collection

Q2 *Some students were studying a field near their school using 0.25m² quadrats. They were interested in three species of plant, A, B and C.*
The quadrat was thrown carefully over their shoulders ten times and the number of plants of each type was recorded each time.
Their results are shown in the table on the right.

Sample number	Number of A	Number of B	Number of C
1	3	12	0
2	7	9	0
3	5	10	2
4	9	7	5
5	1	0	2
6	0	0	0
7	2	4	3
8	5	5	1
9	6	3	0
10	2	0	2

a) What *area* (in m²) was sampled in total?

....

b) How many plants of species A were counted altogether? ....

c) *The species density is the number of plants found per m².*

Work out the species density for species A. ....

....

d) If the area of the whole field was 75m², estimate how many of species A there were in the

whole field. ....

e) Work out the species density and estimated total number for species B and C.

Density of species B = ...

....

Total number of species B = ...

Density of species C = ...

....

Total number of species C = ...

Q3 *There are several methods available to capture animals humanely for study. The pooter (right) is used for insects and spiders and other tiny creatures.*

Look at the picture of the pooter. How does it work?

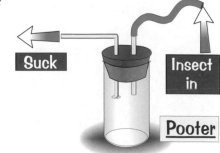

....

....

....

Questions on Data Collection

Q4 Suppose you wanted to estimate the *number of each species* of tree in a woodland.

a) What *problems* might you have if you used a quadrat to do this? ....

....

....

Using a Line Transect for sampling can overcome the problems of a Quadrat. A length of string is marked off at regular intervals and tied between two sticks along part of the habitat. Wherever a plant touches one of the marks, its distance along the line is recorded.

b) Why is a line transect a better method for sampling the species in a woodland? ....

....

c) What problems still remain with this method? ....

....

Q5 *Populations of animals are more difficult to estimate than populations of plants. One way to estimate a population of animals is the capture–recapture method. Some animals are caught, marked with non-toxic paint, and released. A day or so later some animals are again caught, and the number of marked animals is counted. The total population is estimated using the formula:*

$$\text{Estimated population} = \frac{\text{Number caught first time} \times \text{Number caught second time}}{\text{Number of marked animals caught second time}}$$

a) Explain why animal populations are more difficult to estimate than plant populations.

....

....

b) *The manager of a fishing lake wanted to estimate the population of trout in the lake.*

Twenty fish were caught, and small rings were clipped onto their fins. The fish were released back into the lake. Two days later, 25 trout were caught. Five of them had rings.

Work out the *estimated* population of trout in the lake, using the formula above. Show all

your working. ....

....

....

12

Questions on Analysis and Interpretation of Data

Tables are a very convenient way to show lots of data, and you may be asked in the Exam to complete or draw up a table. Remember these simple tips for drawing clear tables:

1. *Draw the lines with a pencil so that unwanted lines or errors can be erased.*

2. *If you are recording measurements, the units should be put in the headings.*

3. *If you are measuring a trend (e.g. the number of bubbles produced by pond weed when a light is shone on it from different distances) it is usual to make the first column the factor you are changing and the second column the factor you are measuring (see example opposite).*

Distance of Light (cm)	Number of Bubbles in One Minute
10	23
15	11
20	6

Q1 *Matthew did an experiment to look at the effect of insulation on the <u>rate of heat loss</u> from beakers containing hot water.*

He took the temperature every minute. His results are shown on the right.

> Both beakers start at 59°C
>
> Control beaker (cb) after 1 min: 45°C
>
> Insulated beaker (ib) after 1 min: 54°C
>
> cb 38°C ib 50°C
> cb 33°C ib 47°C
>
> Final readings: cb 28°C and ib 44°C

a) Draw up a suitable table for Matthew's results in the box below, and put his results into your table.

b) Explain why your table is a better way of showing these results. ....

....

....

SECTION ONE — BASIC SKILLS

Questions on Analysis and Interpretation of Data

Q2 *Pie charts are very useful for showing data that are unrelated to another factor, e.g. the percentage of different types of trees in a wood, or the percentage contribution of different sources of acid rain gases.*

It seems obvious, but remember that there are 360° in a full circle. In examinations, you will normally be given guide lines to help plot or interpret the pie chart (see diagrams below). These are normally ruled at 18° intervals.

a) How many 18° segments are there in a circle? ....

b) Look at the unlabelled pie charts below.

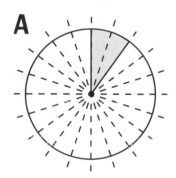 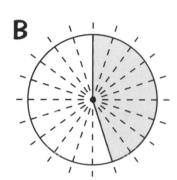

What percentage of the full circle does the shaded segment in each case represent?

The percentage of A shaded is ....

The percentage of B shaded is ....

Q3 A can of baked beans contains 22g of protein, 11g of sugars, 19g of starch and 22g of fibre.

a) Work out the total mass of the contents. ....

b) What percentage of the total mass does each nutrient constitute? ....

....

....

....

c) Draw a *table* and *pie chart* for this information in the box and circle provided below.

 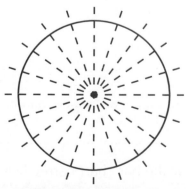

Questions on Analysis and Interpretation of Data

When drawing pie charts, the different segments should be labelled by writing the label outside the circle next to its segment. It often makes the chart clearer if you also write the value with the label, e.g. "power stations 34%". To make things clear, draw a line from the label to the small segments.

Q4 Complete the four pie charts below by shading the proportions shown next to them.

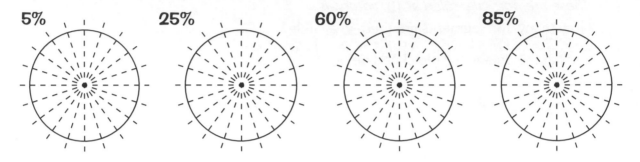

5%   **25%**   **60%**   **85%**

Q5 *The pie chart on the right shows the contributions of various countries to the world's greenhouse gas emissions. Work out the percentage of greenhouse gas emission for each country, including "others":*

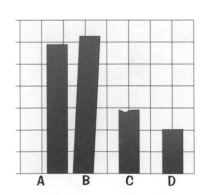

USA .... %   Russia .... %

China .... %   UK .... %

Japan .... %   Others .... %

Q6 *A bar chart is a good way to present data showing a trend or pattern. It is useful for comparisons. In the Exam you may have to draw a bar chart or complete one given to you. Label the axes including units of measurement where appropriate — and draw the bar lines with a ruler.*

Study Fig. 1, the chart on the right.

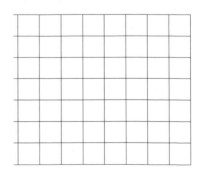

a) *The chart is meant to show the numbers of Aphids, Butterflies, Caterpillars, and Dragonflies seen during a survey. There were 20 Dragonflies. There are several things wrong with this chart. What are they?*

....

....

....

....

b) Redraw the bar chart correctly in the grid opposite.

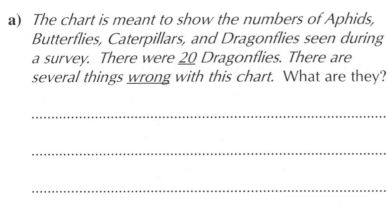

Questions on Analysis and Interpretation of Data

A line graph shows trends and patterns where both the variables are continuous — like temperature and time. You may well have to draw one in the Exam, so it's a good idea to get some practice in now.

Plot the points carefully and label the axes including units of measurement. If the points are not on a straight line, draw a smooth curve through them.

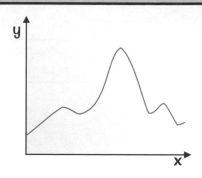

Q7 For each of the following data sets, state whether a pie chart, bar chart or line graph is the most appropriate:

a) *heights* of children in a class. ....

b) *composition* of gases in exhaled air. ....

c) *composition* of gases in inhaled and exhaled air. ....

d) *change* in temperature as a beaker of water cools down. ....

Q8 *To plot a useful frequency histogram, you need to decide on a suitable bin width (e.g. 32-34, 35-37, etc.) when tallying the data. If the bin width is too small then every item might get its own bar, but if it is too big, then every item might contribute to a single bar!*
The table below gives the lengths of 24 leaves.

Length of Leaf (mm)					
32	47	44	43	41	38
36	48	44	43	41	39
37	49	44	43	42	40
38	49	45	43	42	40

a) What is the *maximum* length? ....

b) What is the *minimum* length? ....

c) What is the difference between the maximum and

minimum length (the range)? ....

c) Decide on a suitable bin width for this data, and explain

why you chose it. ....

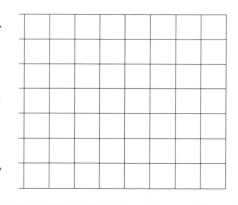

....

d) Use the grid opposite to draw a bar chart of the leaf sizes,

using the bin width you chose in part c).

Questions on Life Processes

Q1 *Plants and animals do things that we call life processes. These are the life processes:*

> movement, reproduction, sensitivity, growth,
> respiration, excretion, nutrition.

a) Identify the life processes that are illustrated by each picture and add labels in the boxes next to each.

b)

Which life processes are not shown in the diagram of the cow?

....

....

....

Q2 *These are pictures of four every day things. All four things can move and make noises.*

a) Why is the toy jack-in-the-box not a living thing?

....

....

....

b) Give one way that all four things are similar to a living thing.

....

Questions on Life Processes

Q3 Use the words to *fill in* the spaces.

move	reproduce	sensitivity	nutrition	excreted	respiration	grow

Living things .... to produce offspring. Animals also .... to

catch food, to find a mate to reproduce and also to escape any predators. As we get

older, we .... to reach our full size. We use energy to do different things.

Releasing energy from food is called .... and eating the food we require

is called .... Any waste produced is .... from our bodies.

Living things must also react to what happens to them. This is called ....

Q4 *This is the life cycle of a cabbage white butterfly.*

a) Name three life processes that are mentioned in the diagram.

....

....

....

b) Write out the life processes that are not mentioned in the diagram.

....

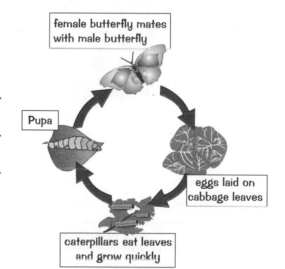

female butterfly mates with male butterfly

Pupa

eggs laid on cabbage leaves

caterpillars eat leaves and grow quickly

c) Draw a similar life cycle for people. Label as many life processes as you can.

Questions on Cells

Q1 *Both the house and the human body are built up of smaller building blocks.*

    a) What do we call the building blocks that make up the:

      i) house? ....

      ii) human body? ....

Q2 a) Add the name labels below to both the plant and animal cell:

| cytoplasm | nucleus | cell membrane |

Animal Cell

Plant Cell

    b) Name two structures that are found in plant cells but not in animal cells.

....

Q3 Complete these sentences with the words in the list below:

cell membrane	cell wall	chloroplasts	nucleus	sap vacuole

All cells have a _____ around their cytoplasm and a

_____. Plant cells also have a strong _____

on their outside and _____ to make food. Plant cells also

have a _____ .

Q4 Write down whether these sentences are true of false:

    a) All cells have a membrane. ....

    b) All cells have a cell wall. ....

    c) Cell walls are made of starch. ....

    d) Cell walls are made of cellulose. ....

    e) Chromosomes are found in the cytoplasm. ....

SECTION TWO — PLANTS

Questions on Cells

Q5 *This is a diagram of a human sperm cell.*

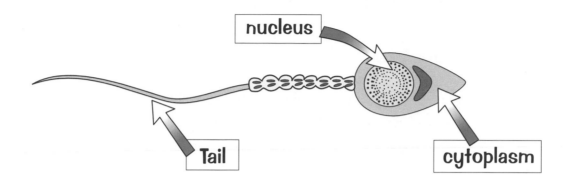

nucleus

Tail

cytoplasm

a) Name one structure that is found in the sperm cell that is not normally found in other cells.

....

b) Circle on the diagram the two labels that are normally found in other animal cells.

Q6 *These are two organisms that live in water. They are both very small and — their whole body is made up of just one cell.*

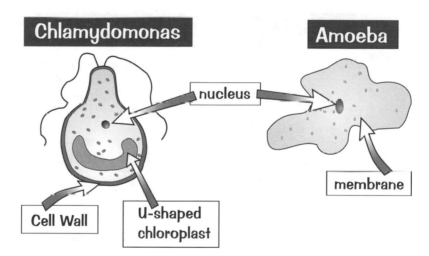

Chlamydomonas

Amoeba

nucleus

Cell Wall

U-shaped chloroplast

membrane

a) Which one is more like a plant?

....

b) Give two reasons for your answer.

....

....

Q7 Write down whether each of these statements is true or false.

a) Nerve cells take messages from one part of the body to another.   ....

b) Egg cells swim to the sperm cells.   ....

c) Leaf cells make food.   ....

d) red blood cells transport oxygen around the body.   ....

Questions on Specialised Cells

Q1 *Eggs are cells. The ostrich egg is the largest cell in the world.*

a) Name three parts of an egg that make it a cell. ....

....

b) What is the job of an egg cell?

....

Q2 These are cells that do special jobs.

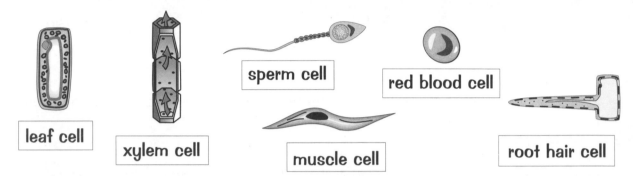

leaf cell   xylem cell   sperm cell   muscle cell   red blood cell   root hair cell

Complete the spaces in the table.

Type of cell	Description of cell	The job the cell does
	Has many chloroplasts	
	Hollow tube	Transports water
Red cell		
	Has a tail and a head	
		For movement
		Absorbs water

Q3 *Jelly fish use stinging cells to protect themselves and to kill their food.*

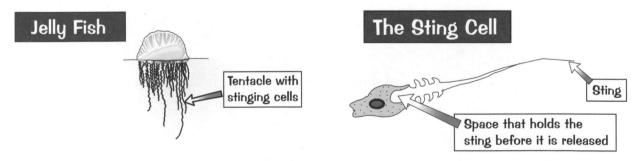

Jelly Fish — Tentacle with stinging cells

The Sting Cell — Sting / Space that holds the sting before it is released

a) On the diagram of the stinging cell label three parts that are also found in other cells.

b) Name one other example of an animal cell and the *special job* it does.

....

SECTION TWO — PLANTS

Questions on Diffusion

Q1 The diagram shows part of a leaf. Gases go in and out of leaves by diffusion.

a) From the diagram, what colour are the arrows that represent the movement of a gas going into the leaf?

....

Which gas do these arrows represent?

....

b) What colour are the arrows that represent the movement of a gas going out of the leaf?

....

Which gas do these arrows represent?

....

Q2 a) *A droplet of coloured liquid was injected into some clear gelatin. The colour diffused through the gelatin.*

Draw arrows on the diagram to show where the colour spreads.

b) Give one example of diffusion in:

    i) plants ....

    ....

    ii) animals ....

    ....

c) Particles from a freshly cut onion diffuse through the air. Draw arrows on the diagram opposite to show the directions that the molecules are moving in.

– onion particles

Questions on Diffusion

Q3   *Gases diffuse (spread) from a high concentration (many particles) to a low concentration (few particles). This occurs in the air sacs in a lung (diagram opposite).*

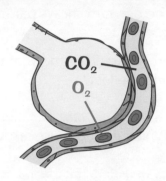

a)   Draw arrow heads on the lines to show which way the oxygen and carbon dioxide particles move.

b)   Complete the table by ticking the correct boxes.

Part of Lung	Concentration of oxygen		Concentration of carbon dioxide	
	Low (few particles)	High (many particles)	Low (few particles)	High (many particles)
Blood vessel going to lung				
Air sac				

Q4   *Diffusion is a very important process in living things. Many parts of living things have become adapted to make diffusion happen more quickly.*

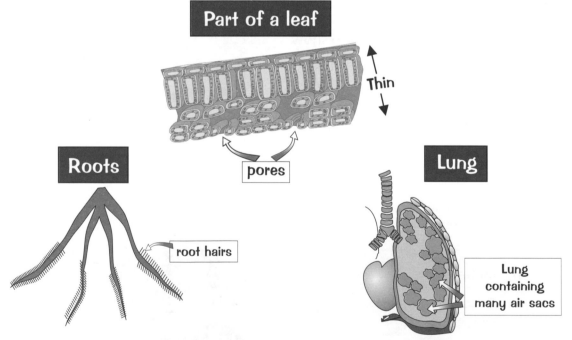

Use the information in the diagrams to give one adaptation in each of these structures.

a)   Roots   ....

b)   Leaves   ....

c)   Lungs   ....

Questions on Diffusion

Q5 *Some cotton wool was soaked in ammonia. The cotton wool was placed at one end of a glass tube. The ammonia turns the pieces of red litmus paper blue.*

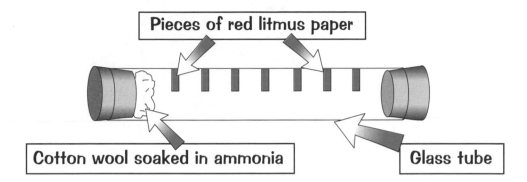

Pieces of red litmus paper

Cotton wool soaked in ammonia

Glass tube

a) **i)** Write number 1 on the piece of litmus paper that changes colour first.

   ii) Write number 7 on the piece of litmus paper that changes last.

b) Draw an arrow on the diagram to show which way the particles move.

c) What do we call the process that spreads out particles in this way? ....

Q6 *An amoeba lives in pond water, which contains the oxygen the amoeba needs for living.*

a) **i)** What is the name of the process by which the oxygen enters the amoeba?

   ....

   ....

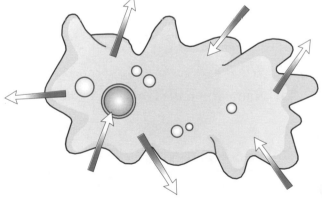

   ii) Write the word oxygen next to one of the arrows that shows this process.

b) Why do living things need oxygen?

....

....

c) Give the name of one substance the amoeba releases in the pond water.

....

Questions on Plant Structure

Q1   *A plant is made up of three parts.*

    a) Label parts A, B and C.

A ....

    X →

B ....

    b) What do we call X? ....

    c) Explain in one sentence what
        each part of the plant does.

C ....

A ....

B ....

C ....

Q2   Draw lines to connect the part of the plant with the correct function it does.

Plant part	→	Function
stems		absorb water
roots		carry leaves
leaves		make food
flowers		seeds are made here

Q3   *The flower contains the reproductive organs of a plant.*

    a) Name the parts labelled A and B.

    A)_____

    B)_____

    b) Why is part A normally very colourful?

    ....

    ....

Q4   *The stem holds the plant upright.*

    a) Why do plants need to be upright? ....

    b) Why is the plant always in the same place in the ground?

    ....

Questions on Plant Structure

Q5 Use the words to *fill in the spaces* (the same word may be used *more* than once).

flower	leaves	mineral salts	petals	roots	reproductive	seeds	stem	water

Plants are made up of three parts, the .... , the stem and the

.... which are found under the ground. The roots hold the plant

firmly in the ground. They also absorb .... with dissolved

.... from the soil. The .... has the job of holding the

plant upright. This helps the leaves to catch more light. The .... are

responsible for making food. The flowers contain the .... parts of the

plant. These are found inside the .... When the flower dies,

.... are released.

Q6 *The diagram below shows the life cycle of a plant. The root is the first part of the seed to grow. Then the leafy shoot appears above the ground. The seed normally contains food to nourish the plant for the first few weeks of growth.*

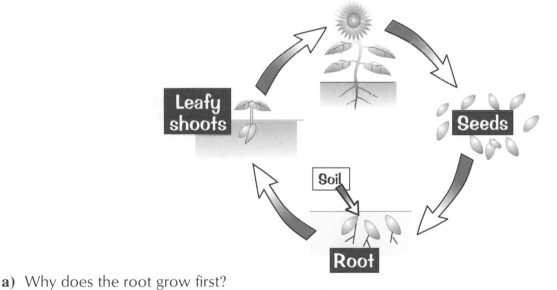

a) Why does the root grow first?

....

b) Why does the plant die if its leaves don't grow above the ground within a few weeks?

....

c) What might happen if the seed is placed very *deep* down in the soil?

....

SECTION TWO — PLANTS

Questions on Plant Structure

Q7 *The diagram shows the parts of a cabbage plant that are eaten by <u>pest</u> animals.*

a) *More pest animals feed off the <u>leaves</u> than the roots.* Why do you think this is?

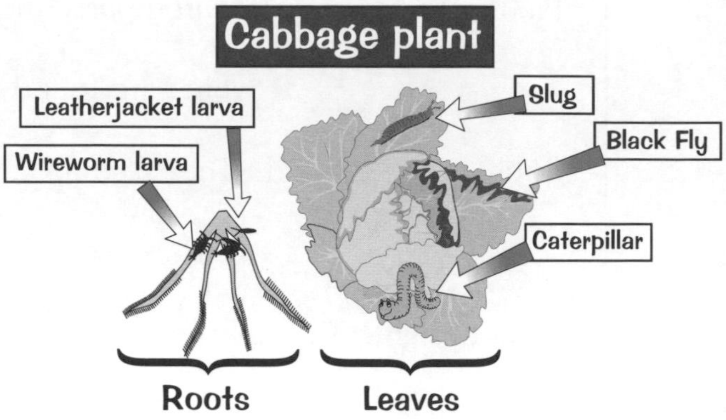

....

....

Cabbage plant

Leatherjacket larva
Wireworm larva
Slug
Black Fly
Caterpillar

Roots   Leaves

b) Why does the plant die when its roots are eaten?

....

....

c) Where would we find the animals that eat the roots of plants?

....

Q8 *The Colorado beetle has spread from Colorado in America to much of Europe. It has been found in the UK since 1901. Both the beetles and their larvae (caterpillar like animals) feed on the leaves of potato plants.*

a) Why are leaves important to a plant?

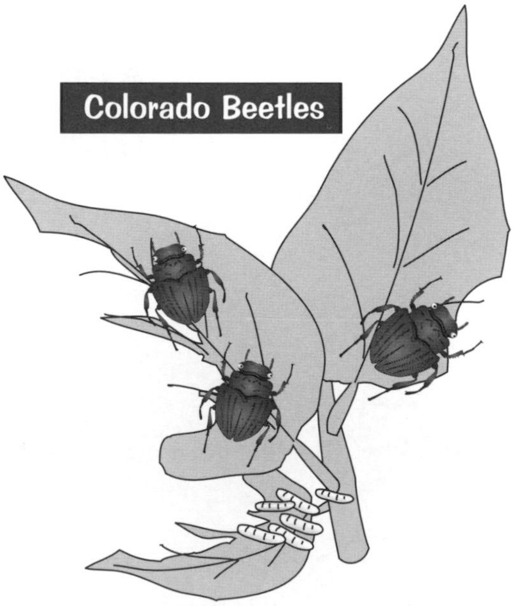

....

....

....

Colorado Beetles

b) What happens to a plant if its leaves are eaten?

....

....

c) Name one other garden animal that eats leaves?

....

Questions on Leaf Structure

Q1 *The diagram opposite shows part of a leaf.*

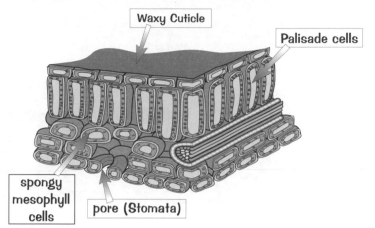

Waxy Cuticle

Palisade cells

spongy mesophyll cells

pore (Stomata)

a) Wax is a waterproof substance. The cuticle on the surface of leaves is made of wax. What is the job of the waxy cuticle?

....

....

b) *Wind currents take moisture away from leaves. The diagram below shows what happens when wind currents hit the surface of leaves.*

Most of the pores that lose water are found on the bottom surface of leaves. Why is this?

....

....

= **Wind currents**

c) *Marram grass has an unusual type of leaf. The leaves of this plant are curled up.*

Draw arrows to show how the wind currents hit this leaf.

Section of Marram grass leaf

Why does having curled leaves help to cut down on the amount of water that is lost?

....

Questions on Leaf Structure

Q2   *Plants whose leaves float on water have more pores on the top surface of their leaves.*

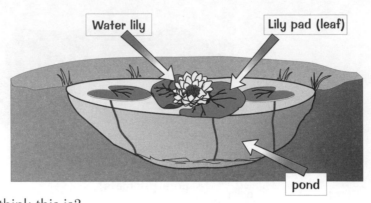

Why do you think this is?

....

....

Q3   *Leaves are darker on their top surface. This is because*
they have more of the green substance,
called chlorophyll, in the cells near the top surface.

   a)   Light from the sun hits the leaves. Draw on
the diagram opposite an arrow showing
the direction the light is coming from.

   b)   Why is it better to have more of the green substance (Chlorophyll) in the top surface of
the leaf?

....

....

Q4   Match the description on the left with the correct part of the leaf.

description	⟶	part

green substance is called

they contain chlorophyll

cells that contain the green substance

chloroplasts

chlorophyll

leaf cells

Questions on Leaf Structure

Q5 *Some plants have green and white areas. This is called variegated leaves.*

Variegated geranium leaf

Green area

White area

Cross section of part of leaf

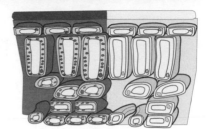

a) Draw an arrow on a leaf cell that is found in the white area and label it W.

b) Draw an arrow on a leaf cell that is found in the green area and label it G.

c) Why are some cells green?

....

....

Q6 Complete the following passage with the words below:

carbon dioxide	chlorophyll	chloroplasts	light	pores	waxy cuticle	xylem

Food is made in the leaves of the plant. Leaf cells have many ....

which contain the green substance .... This substance absorbs

.... The gas .... diffuses easily through spaces

inside the leaf cells. To make sugar, water is also needed. Water is taken to the leaf

by .... cells. To stop water being lost, the surface of the leaf is

covered by a .... To let gases move in and out of the

leaf, there are many .... These are called stomata and are

mainly found on the bottom surface of leaves.

Q7 Most of these words have something to do with leaves. From each line of words, ring the one that does not.

a) leaf   pores   root   waxy cuticle

b) carbon dioxide   sulphuric acid   oxygen   water

c) chlorophyll   sunlight   food   petals

d) veins   bark   pores   chloroplasts

Questions on Transpiration

Q1 *The diagram shows how water is lost from a pore in a leaf.*

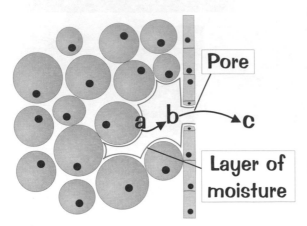

Pore

a b →c

Layer of moisture

a) Tick the correct boxes.

Process	Diffusion	Evaporation
a to b		
b to c		

b) What do we call these kind of pores?

....

Q2 In the experiment below, the air bubble moves up as water is drawn into the stem.
Put a tick or a cross to show correct and incorrect sentences.

a) Losing water from the leaves is called transpiration. ☐

b) More water is lost from the leaves in damper air. ☐

c) Less water is lost from the leaves in drier air. ☐

d) More water is lost in windy conditions. ☐

e) The name of a pore in the leaves is xylem. ☐

Leafy shoot

glass tube

Beaker of warm water

Air bubble

Q3 Complete the following passage using the words below:

cuticle	hot	roots	stomata	transpiration	windy

Water moves from the soil to the .... and then up the stem to

the leaves. Leaves have pores called .... Plants can lose water

from the pores in the leaves. Water is lost more quickly in .... ,

dry and .... conditions. Leaves are covered by a waxy

.... to stop too much water being lost.

Questions on Transpiration

Q4 *This experiment shows water being lost from a clay pot.*
Clay pots have a large number of tiny holes.

a) How is the pot similar to a leaf?

....

b) Give one way that the pot is different from the leaf.

....

c) Say how each of these conditions affects the amount
of water lost from the pot.

i) very damp air ....

ii) very hot air ....

iii) air that is not moving ....

Clay Pot with tiny holes

Water

Capillary tube

Air bubble

Beaker of warm water

Q5 *Before a cutting grows roots, we often remove its leaves and cover it with a plastic bag.*
Without roots, plants find it difficult to get enough water.

a) Where do plants get their water from?

....

b) Why does it help the plant if we remove the leaves?

....

c) Why do we place a plastic bag around a cutting?

....

....

....

Plastic bag

Stem cutting with no leaves

Q6 Find the following words in the word search.

XYLEM

STOMATA

LEAVES

WILTING

TRANSPIRATION

E	A	B	Z	K	X	X	O	P	Q	A	J	H	I
P	O	B	T	S	Y	Y	K	S	E	A	U	U	F
Q	Z	B	O	K	L	Z	T	E	J	G	G	W	V
I	H	M	N	L	E	O	R	J	B	N	T	E	W
J	I	N	M	O	M	D	Q	C	S	I	S	M	R
O	L	L	E	A	V	E	S	I	E	T	D	Z	X
O	H	T	T	M	U	U	Z	H	R	L	Q	N	Y
T	R	A	N	S	P	I	R	A	T	I	O	N	P
T	P	P	O	O	A	Y	S	K	P	W	L	M	O

Questions on Transport Systems in Plants

Q1   *Plants get their water from the soil. This water is later lost to the atmosphere.*

a)   Use these words to complete the flow diagram.

leaves	roots	stem

SOIL ⟹ _____ ⟹ _____ ⟹ _____ ⟹ ATMOSPHERE

b) i)   What cells transport water? ....

ii)   What else do these cells carry? ....

c)   What cells carry sugar (dissolved food)? ....

Q2   *The diagram shows the path water takes through a plant.*

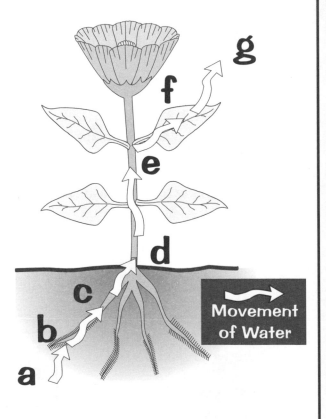

Movement of Water

a)   What carries water from **d** to **f**?

....

b)   To get to **g**, water escapes from little holes in the leaves.

i)   What are these holes called?

....

ii)   What do we call this process?

....

c)   Food is made in the leaves and stored in the roots.

i)   What cells carry the food?

....

ii)   Draw arrows to show the journey of the food.

iii) Colour the arrows showing the journey of food in red and the journey of water in blue.

iv) Add a key of all the arrows to the diagram.

Questions on Transport Systems in Plants

Q3 *This is a diagram of a plum tree. The plums are full of sugar which is made in the leaves of the tree.*

a) How does the sugar get from the leaves to the plums?

....

....

....

The reason fruits like plums are swollen is because they are also full of water.

b) i) Where did the water originally come from?

....

ii) How does the water get to the plum fruits?

....

Q4 *Opposite is a section of a stem, showing the xylem and phloem cells.*

phloem cell

xylem cell

a) What is the job of the xylem cells?

....

....

b) What is the job of the phloem cells?

....

c) Why do the ends of the xylem and phloem cells have a large opening?

....

d) Why are xylem and phloem cells hollow?

....

e) Why are xylem and phloem cells sometimes called the 'plumbing' of the plant?

....

Questions on Photosynthesis

Q1 *The diagram shows what the leaves need to make food.*

  a) Use the words in the box below to fill in the
    blanks on the diagram.

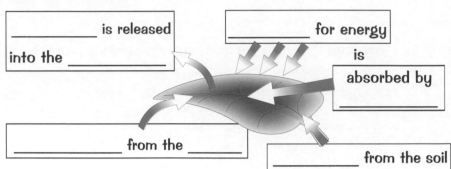

| chlorophyll   air |
| oxygen   air |
| carbon dioxide |
| sunlight   water |

_____ is released
into the _____

_____ for energy
is
absorbed by _____

_____ from the _____

_____ from the soil

  b) Name the process involved in making food.

    ....

  c) What is the name of the food produced?

    ....

Q2 *A variegated plant (its leaves have two colours) was placed in a dark cupboard for 48 hours
    to use up all of its starch. One of its leaves was then covered with a strip of black card
    across the middle. The plant was placed in the light for 24 hours. The leaf was then tested
    for starch.*

  a) Shade in the areas on the unlabelled leaf to
    show where the *starch* was found.

  b) i) What *indicator substance* is used to test a
      leaf for starch?

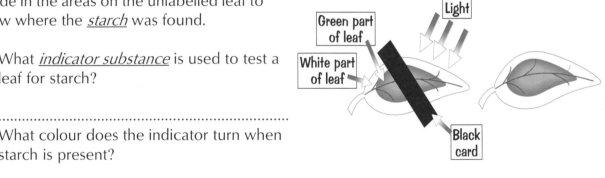

Green part
of leaf

White part
of leaf

Light

Black
card

    ....

  ii) What colour does the indicator turn when
      starch is present?

    ....

  c) Why was it necessary to get rid of the starch from the leaves?

    ....

  d) Tick the correct conclusion(s) that can be drawn from this experiment.

    ... carbon dioxide is needed for photosynthesis   ... chlorophyll is needed for photosynthesis

    ... light is needed for photosynthesis   ... water is needed for photosynthesis

Q3 Complete the following equation for photosynthesis:

_____ _____ + _____ ⟹ _____ + _____

Questions on Photosynthesis

Q4   Complete the table, to show the differences between photosynthesis and respiration.

	Photosynthesis	Respiration
Raw materials used		
End products		
Purpose of process		

Q5   *Adam set up a bottle garden. Inside the bottle he grew some plants and placed a butterfly he'd caught in his garden. He knew the butterfly fed on sugar, so he placed a dish of sugary water inside the bottle. Just before going on a two week holiday to Corfu, Adam caught another butterfly. He placed this butterfly in another bottle, but he did not have time to add the plants. The diagrams show what he saw when he returned from holiday.*

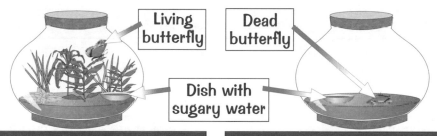

Living butterfly   Dead butterfly   Dish with sugary water

First bottle garden set on window sill   Second bottle garden set on window sill

a) Why did the butterfly in the second bottle die?

....

....

b) Besides its droppings, what does the first butterfly produce that will help the plants to grow?

....

Q6   *A plant was left in a dark cupboard for 48 hours to make sure it had no starch in its leaves. The plant was then set up in a bell jar <u>as shown in the diagram</u>. The apparatus was left for 24 hours after which the leaves tested with iodine.* Place ticks in the correct boxes in the table.

Leaf	Turns blue/black	Has starch
A		
B		
C		
D		

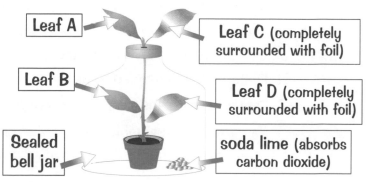

Leaf A
Leaf C (completely surrounded with foil)
Leaf B
Leaf D (completely surrounded with foil)
Sealed bell jar
soda lime (absorbs carbon dioxide)

Questions on Nutrition

Q1 a) Match up the animal groups below to their correct descriptions:

Groups
carnivores are...
omnivores are...
herbivores are...

Descriptions
...animals that can eat both plants and animals
...animals that eat other animals
...animals that eat plants

b) Give an example of each type of animal.

Example of a *herbivore:* ....

Example of a *carnivore:* ....

Example of an *omnivore:* ....

Q2 Complete the sentences below about three nutrients. Choose the correct words from this list.

cell membranes	growth	energy	proteins	fats

Carbohydrates are needed to provide .... for the body.

.... are needed for .... and repair.

Energy is supplied by .... , which are also needed to make

....

Q3 *You should be able to remember foods that are good sources of the three main nutrients.*

a) Write down two examples of foods that are good sources of *carbohydrate*.

Food 1 .... Food 2 ....

b) Write down two examples of foods that are good sources of *protein*.

Food 1 .... Food 2 ....

c) Write down two examples of foods that are good sources of *fat*.

Food 1 .... Food 2 ....

Q4 *We need 20–30g of dietary fibre (roughage) a day.*
A can of baked beans contains over 20g of dietary fibre.

a) Put a tick ✓ in the box ☐ next to each correct sentence about dietary fibre:

☐ Dietary fibre is needed to provide our bodies with carbohydrates for energy.

☐ Dietary fibre helps to prevent constipation if we eat enough of it.

☐ Raw fruit and vegetables are good sources of dietary fibre.

b) One sentence is incorrect. Write down a correct version of it in the space below.

....

Questions on Nutrition

Q5 *Vitamins have a part to play in the chemical reactions inside the body.*
They are only needed in small amounts, but without them we would not be healthy.
Circle the correct words in each of the <u>underlined</u> pairs in these sentences about vitamins.

  a) Vitamins are needed in <u>small</u> / <u>large</u> amounts to keep us healthy.

  b) Oranges and lemons are good sources of <u>vitamin C</u> / <u>vitamin D</u>.

  c) Eggs and fish liver oil are good sources of <u>vitamin C</u> / <u>vitamin D</u>.

Q6 *Minerals are very important in maintaining a healthy body. Match the different types of food to the minerals they provide:*

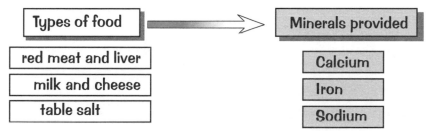

Q7 *It is often recommended that we drink plenty of water, and some foods also contains water. Why is water so important in our diet?*

....

Q8 *Study these food labels from some cheese and pasta packets, then answer the questions.*

  a) Suggest one benefit of eating lots of cheese.

....

  b) Suggest one problem with eating lots of cheese.

....

  c) Suggest one benefit of eating lots of pasta.

....

  d) Suggest one problem with eating lots of pasta.

....

  e) Explain why eating some pasta with some cheese sprinkled over the top might be better than just eating cheese or pasta on their own.

....

....

MURINE BRAND GRATED CHEESE

Nutritional information	
Typical values	Per 100g
Carbohydrate	0.6g
Protein	25.0g
Fat	34.4g
Fibre	less than 0.1g

PATA'S ITALIAN PASTA HELICES

Nutritional information	
Typical values	Per 100g
Carbohydrate	27.4g
Protein	4.6g
Fat	0.4g
Fibre	0.9g

Q9 Circle the correct word from the <u>underlined</u> words in this sentence about balanced diets:
A balanced diet means eating proteins, fats, carbohydrates, vitamins, minerals, dietary fibre and water in <u>large</u> / <u>small</u> / <u>correct</u> amounts to maintain good health.

Questions on Food Tests

Q1   Match the four substances to the correct test which identifies the substance.

substance	⟹	indicator test
fat can be detected using		Benedict's reagent
protein can be detected using		the emulsion test
starch can be detected using		the Biuret test
sugars can be detected using		iodine solution

Q2   Iodine solution is used in food tests. What colour would you see when it is added to:

a) Sugar?   ....

b) Starch?   ....

c) Protein?   ....

Q3   In the table opposite, complete the starting colour and end result for a _positive test_ using Benedict's reagent

colour at start	....
⬇	
end result	....

Q4   The method for the _emulsion_ test is given below. Unfortunately, the instructions have become muddled up. Write the four sentences in the _correct_ order.

Food is put in a test tube.	Some water is added to the test tube.

Ethanol is added, and the test tube is shaken.   The solution is filtered.

....

....

....

....

Q5   What would you expect to see when the emulsion test gives a positive result?

....

Q6   Complete the instructions for the biuret test below. Choose from this list of words:

purple   shake   sodium hydroxide   protein   copper sulphate
The biuret test can be used to detect protein in food. You put some food in a test tube, and add some .... You then give it a .... , and add some .... (this is blue). If it goes a .... colour, it means that .... is present.

SECTION THREE — HUMAN BIOLOGY PART ONE

Questions on The Digestive System

Q1   Use the information below to name these parts of the digestive system. One has been done for you.

Name	Appearance
large intestine	broad rippled tube
gullet	long tube leading from the mouth to the stomach
pancreas	gland with rippled edges
small intestine	coiled narrow tube, 3-5cm in diameter, about 6-7m long
stomach	large container for food - holds about 1 litre

....

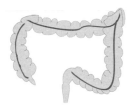

Liver

....

....

....

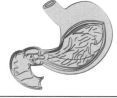

....

....

Q2   Match each part of the body to its correct function.

Part of the Body

the large intestine

the oesophagus (gullet)

the mouth

the stomach

the small intestine

the liver

the pancreas

Function

makes digestive enzymes, and is where digested food is absorbed into the blood

contains teeth to cut and grind food

is where water is absorbed and faeces are stored

joins the mouth with the stomach

makes digestive enzymes and acid

makes insulin and digestive enzymes

stores excess sugar, makes bile, and removes poisons from the blood

SECTION THREE — HUMAN BIOLOGY PART ONE

40

<u>Questions on The Digestive System</u>

Q3 The diagrams below show the four main types of teeth.

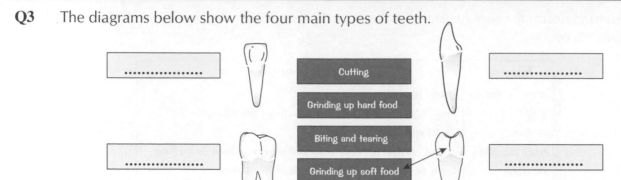

- Cutting
- Grinding up hard food
- Biting and tearing
- Grinding up soft food

a) Write the correct names against each tooth. Choose from: incisor, canine, premolar, molar.

b) Draw a line to link each tooth with its correct function (job). One has been for you already.

Q4 Write the names of each part of the digestive system in the correct boxes below. Choose from the words in the box at the bottom of the page. One of them, the gall bladder, has been done for you.

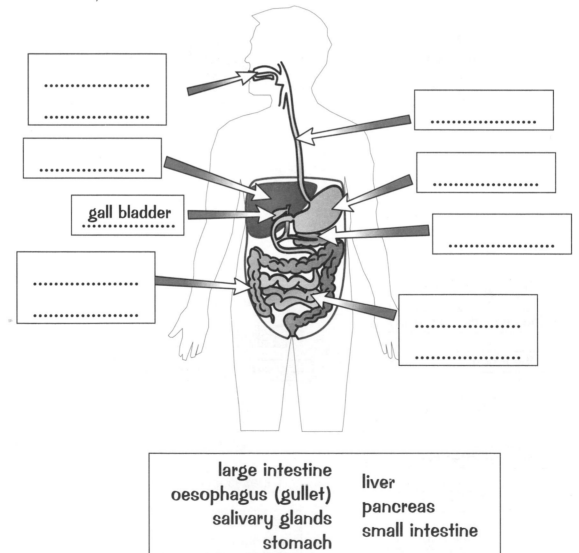

gall bladder

large intestine
oesophagus (gullet)
salivary glands
stomach
liver
pancreas
small intestine

Questions on The Digestive System

Q5 Complete this crossword using the clues given below.

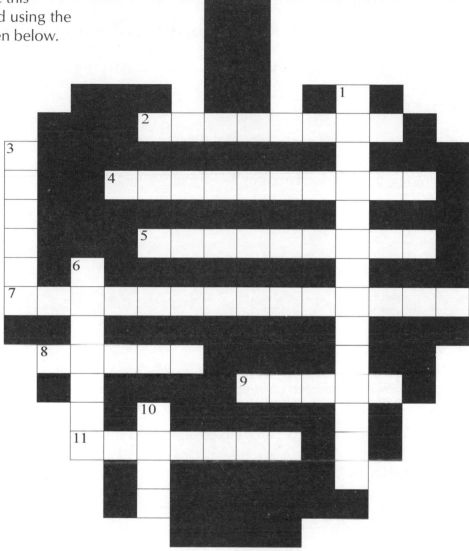

Across

2. Insulin and digestive enzymes are made here (8)

4. The gullet by another name (10)

5. The process by which food is broken down into small particles for absorption into the bloodstream (9)

7. Absorption of broken down food happens here (5,9)

8. This organ makes bile (5)

9. Look after them — they start the process of digestion (5)

11. Produces hydrochloric acid (7)

Down

1. Faeces are stored here before going out of the anus (5,9)

3. Back teeth for grinding (6)

6. Doggy teeth for biting and tearing? (7)

10. This is broken down by the digestive system (4)

SECTION THREE — HUMAN BIOLOGY PART ONE

42

Questions on Digestive Enzymes

Q1 Circle the correct words from each underlined pair in the following sentences:

   a) A catalyst is a substance that is produced by / speeds up chemical reactions.

   b) A catalyst is used /not used up during the reaction. It can be used only once / more than once.

   c) Different reactions need the same catalyst / different catalysts. Enzymes are artificial / biological catalysts. Enzymes are proteins / metals.

Q2 Look at your correct answers to Question 1. Explain what enzymes are, and what they do.

   ....

   ....

   ....

Q3 a) Put a tick in the box next to each correct sentence about digestion:

   ☐ In digestion, large molecules are broken down into small molecules.

   ☐ Digestive enzymes slow down digestion.

   ☐ The digestive system provides the right conditions for digestive enzymes to work well.

   b) One sentence is incorrect. Write down a correct version of it in the space below.

   ....

Q4 *Gastric juice is added to food when it reaches the stomach. This juice contains an acid.*

   a) Name the acid secreted by the stomach.

   ....

   b) Estimate the pH of the stomach contents and give a reason for your answer.

   ....

   c) Give two reasons why the stomach secretes this acid

   ....

   ....

SECTION THREE — HUMAN BIOLOGY PART ONE

Questions on Digestive Enzymes

Q5 *You need to know about <u>three</u> types of digestive enzymes.*

Match the digestive enzymes to the substance that they break down into:

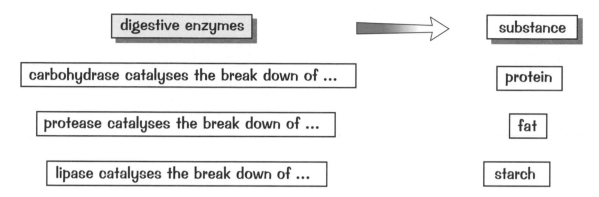

| digestive enzymes | ⟹ | substance |

carbohydrase catalyses the break down of ...

protein

protease catalyses the break down of ...

fat

lipase catalyses the break down of ...

starch

Q6 *It's important to know what the nutrients are broken down into.*

Match the three nutrients to the correct substance that they break down into.

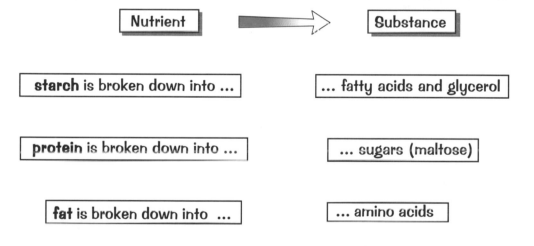

| Nutrient | ⟹ | Substance |

starch is broken down into ...

... fatty acids and glycerol

protein is broken down into ...

... sugars (maltose)

fat is broken down into ...

... amino acids

Q7 Look at your answers to questions 5 and 6. They will help you to complete the sentences below using the words from this box:

fatty	sugars	catalyses	protease
starch	breakdown	amino	glycerol

Carbohydrase catalyses the breakdown of .... into

.... catalyses the .... of proteins

into .... acids. Lipase .... the breakdown of fats into

.... acids and ....

Q8 The <u>*small intestine*</u> and the <u>*pancreas*</u> both make all three types of digestive enzymes.

What are these three types of digestive enzymes called?

a) ....   b) ....   c) ....

SECTION THREE — HUMAN BIOLOGY PART ONE

Questions on Digestive Enzymes

Q9 *The salivary glands only produce one type of enzyme, called carbohydrase. The stomach only produces one type of enzyme as well.*

a) What is this enzyme called? ....

b) What does this enzyme do?

....

Q10 The diagram below is a flow chart for the digestive system.

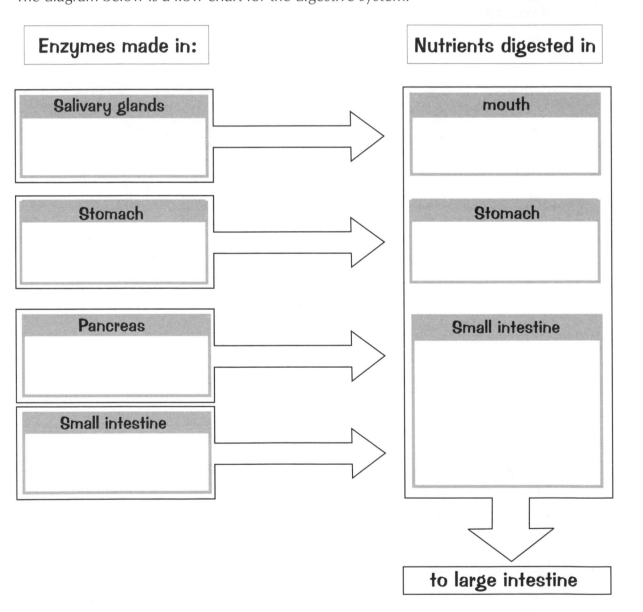

a) In the boxes in the "enzymes" column, write down the name of each enzyme produced by the salivary glands, the stomach, the pancreas, and the small intestine.

b) In the boxes in the "nutrients" column, write down the name of each nutrient digested.

Questions on Absorption of Food

Q1   *Angela was given a mixture of sand and sugar in a beaker.*
She was asked to separate the sand from the sugar. Angela decided to use the methods
shown in the diagrams below to do this.

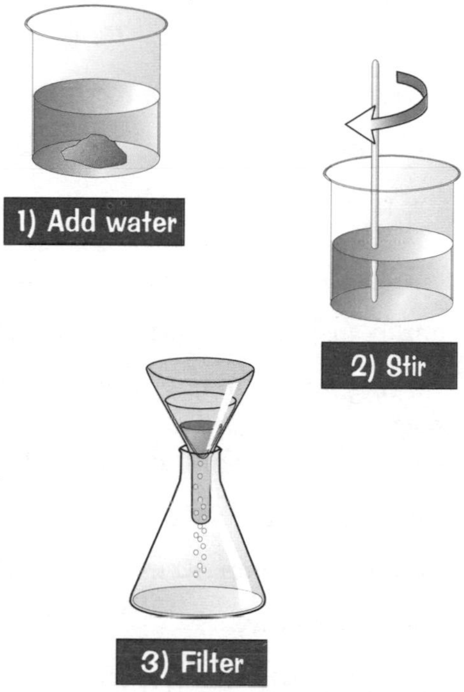

   a) In steps 1 and 2, what happens to the sand?

   ....

   ....

   b) At the end of step 3, where will Angela find
   the sand?

   ....

   c) In steps 1 and 2, what happens to the salt?

   ....

   d) At the end of step 3, where will Angela find the salt?

   ....

1) Add water

2) Stir

3) Filter

   e) The pores in filter paper are so tiny that for particles to pass through it they must be
   dissolved in water. Why can sand be separated from salt using Angela's method?

   ....

   ....

Q2   Put these substances into the correct columns in the table. Some substances are already in
   the table for you.

amino acids	starch	fat	sugar	fatty acids

soluble (dissolve in water)	insoluble (do not dissolve in water)
some proteins	some proteins
glycerol	

Questions on Absorption of Food

Q3 *The molecules produced by digestion can be absorbed into the body.*

a) Where does most absorption of digested food happen? Circle the correct answer below:

the oesophagus (gullet) / the stomach / the small intestine / the large intestine

b) Where is most water from food absorbed? Circle the correct answer below:

the oesophagus (gullet) / the stomach / the small intestine / the large intestine

Q4 *Rob did an experiment to show the movement of food molecules through the walls of a <u>model intestine</u>.* The diagram opposite shows what he did.

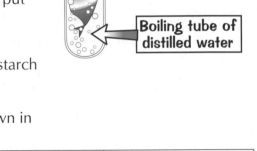

Visking tubing containing starch suspension and sugar solution

Boiling tube of distilled water

Rob made a bag using *Visking* tubing, and put a mixture of starch suspension and sugar solution into the bag. He put the bag into a boiling tube of distilled water.

Rob tested the contents of the bag, and the water, for starch and sugar at the start of his experiment.

He did this again 30 minutes later. His results are shown in the table below.

a) What did Rob find in the water at the end of the experiment?

....

b) What did Rob find in the bag at the end of the experiment?

time (minutes)	contents of bag		water	
	starch	sugar	starch	sugar
0	✔	✔	✘	✘
30	✔	✔	✘	✔

....

c) Why did Rob test the water at the start of the experiment?

....

....

d) Suggest why only one of the substances was able to pass through the Visking tubing.

....

....

e) Which part of the intestine does the Visking tubing represent? Circle the correct answer:

the oesophagus (gullet) / the stomach / the small intestine / the large intestine.

f) What does the water in the boiling tube represent?

....

Questions on Absorption of Food

Q5 *The digestive system breaks down food into small molecules that dissolve in water.*
For revision, match the food being digested to the correct substance that is created.

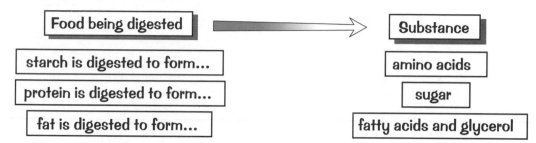

| Food being digested | ⟶ | Substance |

starch is digested to form...

protein is digested to form...

fat is digested to form...

amino acids

sugar

fatty acids and glycerol

Q6 Solve the absorption crossword.

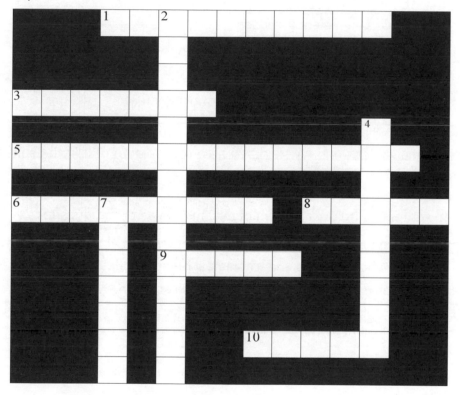

Across

1. Passing digested food into the blood (10)

3. A substance that can dissolve is called this (7)

5. Water is absorbed here (5,9)

6. The break down of food into small particles (9)

8. Digested food is absorbed into this (5)

9. This size of particle can be absorbed (5)

10. This size of particle can't be absorbed (5)

Down

2. Digested food is absorbed here (5,9)

4. Substances that can't dissolve are this (9)

7. These help make small molecules from large ones (7)

SECTION THREE — HUMAN BIOLOGY PART ONE

Questions on Deficiency Diseases

Q1 a) What does it mean to say a diet is *deficient* in nutrients such as vitamins, minerals or proteins?

....

b) What does *deficiency disease* mean?

....

Q2 Match the nutrient deficiency with the disease that can result from it.

Deficiency	⟹	Disease

vitamin D deficiency causes   rickets

protein deficiency causes   kwashiorkor

vitamin C deficiency causes   scurvy

Q3 a) Put a tick in the box next to each correct sentence about minerals:

☐ Iron and calcium are minerals needed for a balanced diet.

☐ Iron is needed to maintain strong bones and teeth.

☐ About 90% of the calcium stored in our body is found in bone.

b) One sentence is incorrect. Write down a correct version of it in the space below.

....

Q4 Read the sentences below about minerals, then answer the questions.

> Minerals need to be in solution so that the intestine can absorb them.
> Some foods, such as cereals and wholemeal bread, contain a substance called phytic acid.
> Phytic acid stops calcium and iron from being in solution.

a) What problem might eating a lot of cereals containing phytic acid cause?

....

b) Why do food manufacturers often put calcium carbonate and iron sulphate into flour?

....

Q5 Circle the correct word from the underlined pair of words in the sentence below.

Iron / calcium is needed to make the haemoglobin found in red blood cells.

Q6 Match the disease to the correct symptoms:

disease	⟹	symptoms

scurvy   bloated abdomen

rickets   loose teeth and bleeding gums

kwashiorkor   bow legs

anaemia   pale skin and tiredness

Q7 Suggest a reason why the majority of people with iron deficiency are women.

....

Questions on The Circulatory System

Q1   *There are two main components of the circulatory system. One organ has a circuit all to itself and its <u>artery</u> carries <u>deoxygenated</u> blood. Which organ is this?*

....

Q2 a) Put a tick in the box next to each correct sentence about the circulatory system:

       ☐ The circulatory system transports nutrients and oxygen from cells in the body.

       ☐ The circulatory system distributes heat and hormones around the body.

       ☐ The circulatory system transports wastes away from the cells in the body.

  b) Write down a correct version of the incorrect sentence in the space below.

....

Q3   *The diagram below shows the main features of the circulatory system. Deoxygenated blood is represented by black lines, and oxygenated blood by grey lines. The arrows show the direction of movement of the blood.*

Use your knowledge and the clues in the diagram to match the labels 1 — 5 with the following blood vessels:

Blood vessels:	Pulmonary vein	Hepatic vein	Renal artery	Aorta	Vena cava

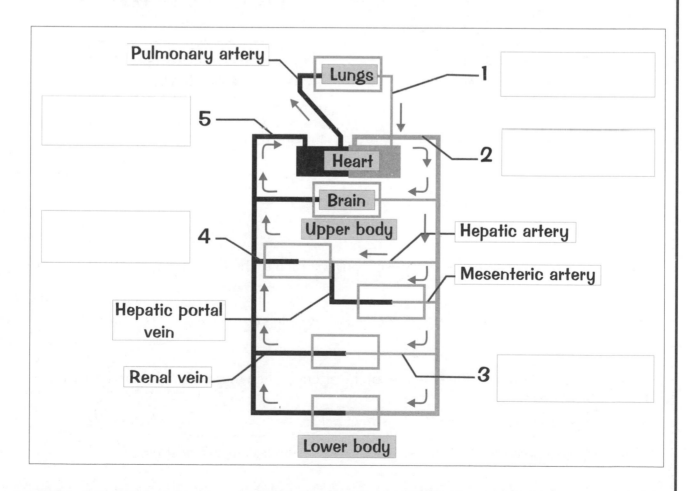

Questions on The Circulatory System

Q4 From the evidence in the diagram and your answers in Question 3, what is the difference between an *artery* and a *vein?* Put a tick in the box next to the correct sentence:

☐ Arteries carry oxygenated blood and veins carry deoxygenated blood.

☐ Veins carry oxygenated blood and arteries carry deoxygenated blood.

☐ Arteries carry blood from the heart and veins carry blood to the heart.

☐ Veins carry blood from the heart and arteries carry blood to the heart.

Q5 What is the function of the heart in the circulatory system?

....

Q6 Why is this system called the circulatory system?

....

Q7 *The diagrams below show a section of healthy artery, and a section of diseased artery.*

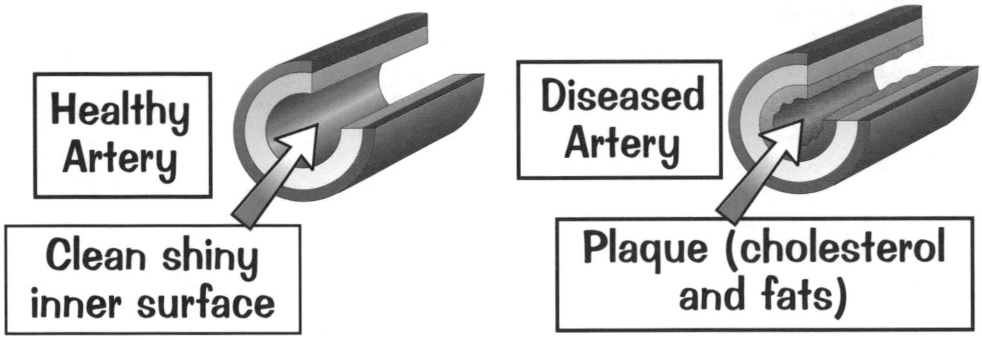
Healthy Artery
Clean shiny inner surface
Diseased Artery
Plaque (cholesterol and fats)

a) What will happen to the flow of blood through the diseased artery?

....

b) Explain your answer to part a).

....

c) If the artery became blocked, what would happen to the tissues supplied by that artery?

....

Q8 *The smooth muscle in the walls of the arteries can contract, especially when you are under stress.*

a) What will happen to the diameter of the arteries when these smooth muscles contract?

....

b) Suggest a possible effect on the circulatory system as a result of stress.

....

Questions on The Circulatory System

Q9   *Mr. Spanner is happily washing his car using a garden hose, then one of his children stands on the hose as a practical joke.*

a) What happens to the hose where the child is standing on it? ....

b) What happens to the flow of water from the hose when the child stands on it?

....

c) Mr. Spanner's garden hose is only about 2cm in diameter, but the Fire Brigade uses really wide hoses for putting out fires. Why does the Fire Brigade use wide hoses instead of narrow ones?

....

....

d) *Our blood vessels are a bit like the garden hose, except they carry blood around the body.*

What would happen to the rate of blood flow in an artery if it narrowed at one point?

....

....

....

Q10   *Mr. Spanner's car ran out of petrol in the middle of nowhere, and he had to push it to the nearest petrol garage.*

The table shows what happened to his heart when he did this exercise.

Study the table, then circle the correct words in each <u>underlined</u> word pair.

	At rest	Pushing Car
Heart rate (beats per minute)	60	150
Stroke volume (cm³)	100	120
Cardiac Output (cm³ per minute)	6000	18000

a) During exercise, the heart rate and stroke volume (volume pumped in one beat) go <u>down</u> / <u>up</u>.

b) During exercise, the cardiac output goes <u>down</u> / <u>up</u>.

c) Fit athletes often have very low resting heart rates because they have a <u>greater number of beats per minute</u> / <u>greater stroke volume</u>.

Questions on The Heart

Q1 *The diagram on the right shows the human heart drawn as a simple engineering drawing, rather than as a cross-section of a real heart.*

— The arrows show the movement of blood.

— The valves are shown in grey.

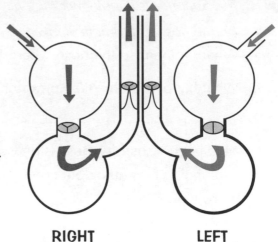

RIGHT   **LEFT**

Circle the correct answers in the questions below.

a) There are 1 / 2 / 3 / 4 chambers in the heart.

b) The upper chambers are called <u>ventricles</u> / <u>atria</u>.

c) The lower chambers are called <u>ventricles</u> / <u>atria</u>.

d) Deoxygenated blood returns from the body to the <u>left</u> / <u>right</u> side of the heart.

e) Oxygenated blood returns from the lungs to the <u>left</u> / <u>right</u> side of the heart.

f) The <u>valves</u> / <u>muscles</u> in the heart make sure that blood flows in the right direction.

Q2 *You may be asked to label the parts of the heart. The diagram below shows a cross-section of the human heart drawn from the front.* Match the labels to the correct names:

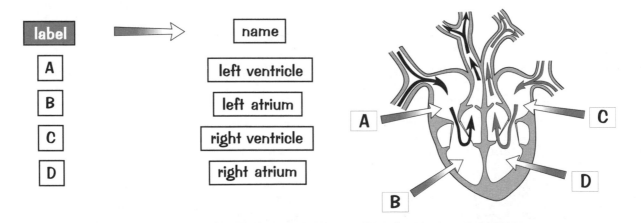

label		name
A		left ventricle
B		left atrium
C		right ventricle
D		right atrium

Q3 *The diagram below shows a cross-section of the human heart, drawn from the front.* Write down these four blood vessels in the correct boxes to complete the labelling.

pulmonary vein

aorta

vena cava

pulmonary artery

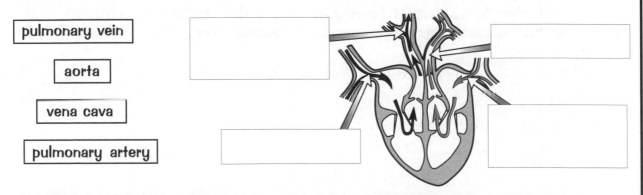

Questions on The Heart

Q4 Complete these sentences about the heart.
Choose from the list of words below.

valves	muscle	body	blood	pumps	wall

The .... of the heart is mainly .... The heart .... blood

around the .... The .... prevent backflow of ....

Q5 *The diagram on the right shows how the heart fits into the circulatory system. The left side pumps blood around the body.*

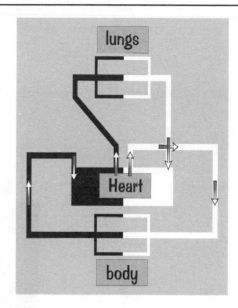

a) Where does the right side pump blood to?

....

b) The blood going to the lungs is at a lower pressure than

the blood going to the rest of the body. Suggest a

reason for this.

....

....

c) The left side of the heart has thicker walls than the right

side. Suggest a reason for this difference.

....

....

d) The heart is often called a double pump, and the circulatory system is often called a

double circulatory system. Why is this?

....

Q6 a) What type of tissue are the walls of the heart made from? ....

b) Explain how you could work this out from your knowledge of how the heart works.

....

....

Questions on The Heart

Q7 The sentences below describe the steps needed for the heart to pump blood. Put a ring around the correct options of <u>underlined</u> words.

Blood enters the heart via [<u>the left</u> / <u>the right</u> / <u>either</u>] [<u>atrium</u> / <u>ventricle</u>].

Blood leaves the heart when either [<u>atrium</u> / <u>ventricle</u>] [<u>contracts</u> / <u>relaxes</u>].

Valves make sure that the [<u>blood</u> / <u>air</u>] flows in the correct direction.

Contractions of the right atrium force blood into the [<u>left</u> / <u>right</u>] [<u>artery</u> / <u>ventricle</u>].

The pulmonary vein is odd in that it carries [<u>oxygenated</u> / <u>deoxygenated</u>] blood

Q8 Complete the crossword. The word answers are all to do with the heart.

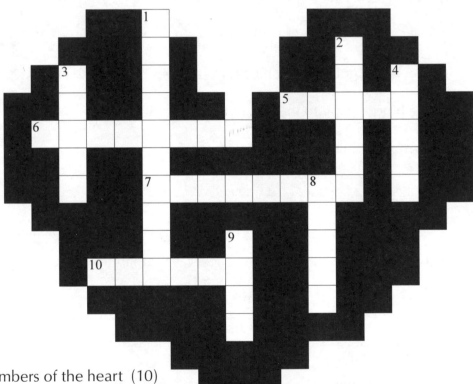

Down

1. The lower chambers of the heart (10)

2. These prevent the backflow of blood (6)

3. The word for more than one atrium (5)

4. These carry blood to the heart (5)

8. This side pumps blood to the lungs (5)

9. This side pumps blood around the body (4)

Across

5. Feel this to check the heart rate (5)

6. These carry blood from the heart (8)

7. There are four of these in the heart (8)

10. The walls of the heart consist mainly of this (6)

SECTION THREE — HUMAN BIOLOGY PART ONE

Questions on Blood Vessels

Q1   Circle the correct words in the <u>underlined</u> pairs in these two sentences about blood vessels.

       Arteries carry blood <u>to</u> / <u>from</u> the heart at <u>low</u> / <u>high</u> pressure.

       Veins carry blood <u>to</u> / <u>from</u> the heart at <u>low</u> / <u>high</u> pressure.

Q2   *The diagrams on the right show cross-sections of blood vessels.*
They are not drawn to scale.

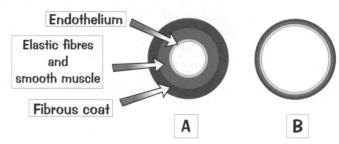

a) What is the space at the centre called?

....

b) One of these blood vessels is an artery, and one is a vein. Which diagram shows an artery?

Diagram   ....

c) Briefly explain how you worked out your answer to part b).

....

....

Q3   *The diagrams A and B opposite show pieces of artery and vein sliced along their length.* They are not drawn to scale.

a) Which diagram, A or B, shows the vein? Diagram   ....

b) What is the name of the extra structure in diagram A?

....

c) What does the structure named in part b) do?

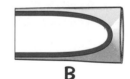

....

d) It is possible to work out which way the blood must be flowing in vessel A.

Work this out, and draw an arrow on the diagram to show the direction of blood flow.

Q4   Complete the sentences below about *capillaries* using the words from this list:

capillaries	out	thin	vessels	narrow	blood	cells

Capillaries are very .... blood .... with ....

walls. Substances needed by the cells pass .... of the ....

through the capillary walls. Substances made by the .... can also pass into

the blood through the walls of the ....

Q5   Which type of blood vessel is the one that gives us a pulse? ....

Questions on The Blood

Q1 a) Match the type of blood cell to the correct description of its function

Blood cell	⟶	Function

red blood cells

platelets

white blood cells

help blood to clot at the site of a wound

transport oxygen from the lungs to the organs

ingest bacteria in the blood

Q2 a) Put a tick in the box next to each correct sentence about *plasma*:

☐ Plasma is a red coloured liquid.

☐ Plasma transports breakdown products of digestion.

☐ Plasma transports oxygen from the organs to the lungs.

☐ Plasma transports platelets.

☐ Plasma transports urea from the liver to the kidneys.

b) Two sentences are incorrect. Write down correct versions of them in the spaces below.

....

....

c) Plasma has other functions that are not listed in part b). Give another function of plasma.

....

Q3 *Three components of the blood consist of cells or fragments of cells.*

a) Write down their names.

1 .... 2 .... 3 ....

b) Only one of these components has a nucleus. Which one? ....

c) The diagram on the right shows one of the cells named in part b).
Write down the names of the parts labelled A, B and C.

Part A ....

Part B ....

Part C ....

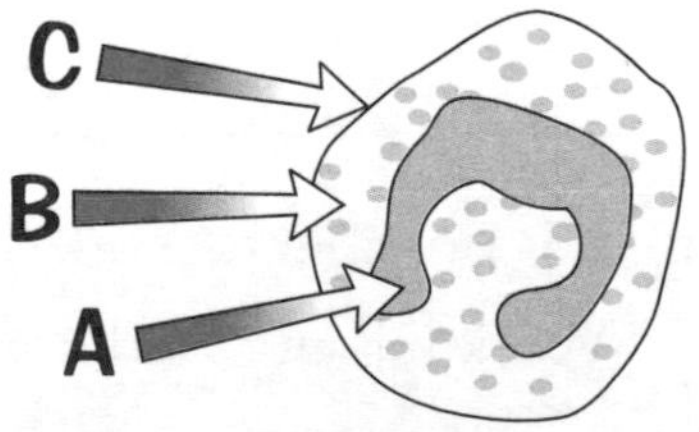

Q4 *Red cells have a shape called a <u>biconcave</u> disc (look at the diagram of a cut away red cell). This gives them a large surface area for their volume.*

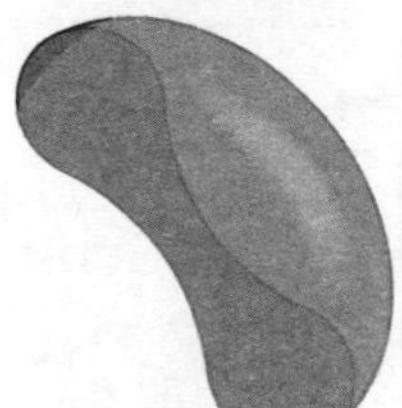

a) Explain how this shape helps the red cell to do its job well.

....

....

b) The cytoplasm of red cells contains haemoglobin.

What does haemoglobin do? ....

c) Red cells in humans and most other mammals have no nucleus. Suggest a reason why.

....

SECTION THREE — HUMAN BIOLOGY PART ONE

Questions on Lungs and Breathing

Q1   In the sentences below circle the correct words in the <u>underlined</u> pairs.

   a) The breathing system takes <u>air</u> / <u>oxygen</u> into and out of the body.

   b) This allows <u>carbon dioxide</u> / <u>oxygen</u> to pass from the air into the bloodstream.

   c) It also allows <u>carbon dioxide</u> / <u>oxygen</u> to pass out of the bloodstream into the air.

Q2   The diagram shows the *thorax*.

   Match up the parts with the correct labels.

   Some parts will have more than one label.

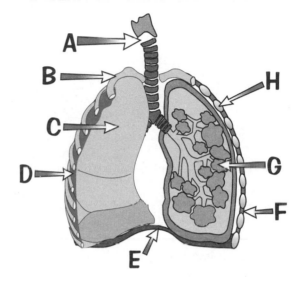

Name of part	label
alveoli	
diaphragm	
intercostal muscles	
lung	
ribs	
trachea	

Q3   *When air is breathed in through the nose or mouth, it passes through parts of the breathing system to the <u>alveoli</u>.*

   Write down these parts of the breathing system in the correct order, starting at the nose:

bronchioles	trachea	bronchi	alveoli

Nose ⟹ .... ⟹ ....

.... ⟸ ....

Q4   Match the part of the breathing system to its correct function.

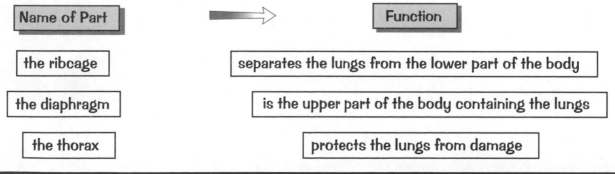

Name of Part	Function

the ribcage	separates the lungs from the lower part of the body
the diaphragm	is the upper part of the body containing the lungs
the thorax	protects the lungs from damage

SECTION THREE — HUMAN BIOLOGY PART ONE

Questions on Lungs and Breathing

Q5 Complete the paragraph below using the words given.

oxygen	carbon dioxide	alveoli	alveolus	Red

Each lung contains millions of tiny air sacs called .... The alveoli

are surrounded by a network of blood capillaries. At each .... ,

.... passes into the blood and .... passes out of

the blood. .... blood cells carry the oxygen to all the cells in the body.

Q6 a) The _trachea_ has rings of cartilage around it. What do these rings of cartilage do?

....

....

b) The trachea splits into smaller air passages called _bronchi_. How many bronchi do each of us have?

Number of bronchi ....

c) What is a bronchiole?

....

d) What are the alveoli?

....

Q7 _Look at the apparatus shown in the diagram opposite. It is often used in science lessons to show how the gas we breathe in is different from the gas we breathe out._
You have to breathe gently in and out through the top tube.

a) Both tubes contain limewater. Which gas does limewater detect?

Name of gas ....

b) When the apparatus is used properly, which tube should contain

very cloudy limewater? Circle the correct answer below:

tube A / tube B

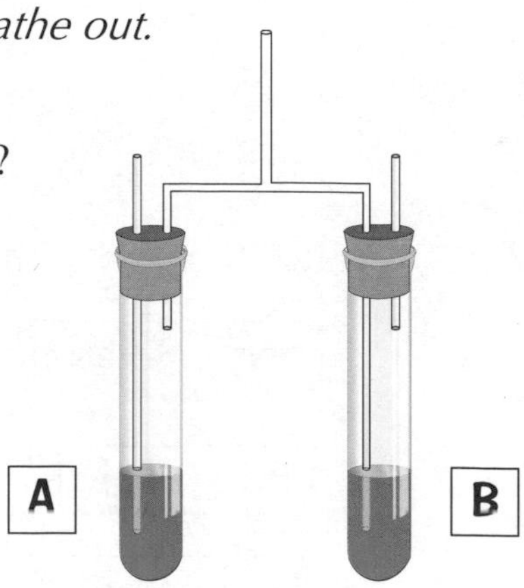

A   B

Questions on Lungs and Breathing

Q8 *The air we breath out has a different composition to the air we breath in.*

Gas	% in inhaled air	% in exhaled air
oxygen		
carbon dioxide		
nitrogen		

Complete the table above to show the percentages of oxygen, carbon dioxide and nitrogen in inhaled and exhaled air. Use the numbers from the box below.

0.04	21	78	16	5	78

Q9 The left hand side of the table below explains what happens when we breathe in. Complete the right hand side of the table to explain what happens when we breathe out. Use these words:

more	downwards	relax	decreases	up	relax	out

Breathing In	Breathing Out
The diaphragm muscles contract.	The diaphragm muscles _____.
This causes the diaphragm to flatten.	This causes the diaphragm to move upwards.
The muscles between the ribs contract.	The muscles between the ribs _____.
This pulls the ribcage upwards.	This pulls the ribcage _____.
The volume of the thorax increases.	The volume of the thorax _____.
The pressure inside the thorax goes down.	The pressure inside the thorax goes _____.
The pressure inside the thorax gets less than atmospheric pressure.	The pressure inside the thorax gets _____ than atmospheric pressure.
Air is pushed into the lungs from outside to make the pressures equal.	Air is pushed _____ of the lungs to make the pressures equal.

Q10 Circle the correct words from the <u>underlined</u> pairs in the sentences below.

Gaseous exchange happens in the <u>trachea</u> / <u>alveoli</u>.

The cilia keep the lungs <u>clean</u> / <u>warm</u>.

The mucous membranes make the air coming into the air passages <u>dry</u> / <u>moist</u> and <u>warm</u> / <u>cold</u>.

60

Questions on Respiration

Q1 Complete the sentences below about respiration using the words from this list:

molecules	all	large	temperature	smaller	contract	plants

Respiration is a process that takes place in .... living cells. Respiration

transfers energy from food .... in animals and .... The

energy from respiration is used to make .... molecules from ....

ones, to let muscles ...., and to keep a constant body ....

Q2 a) Put a tick in the box ☐ next to each correct sentence about respiration:

☐ Plants cannot respire.

☐ Respiration means getting air in and out of the lungs.

☐ Respiration releases energy from food molecules in cells.

b) Write down the correct versions of the sentences above that are wrong.

....

....

Q3 a) Complete the following word equation to describe respiration.

Glucose + ... ⟹ .... + water (+ energy).

b) Look at your equation. What two substances are needed for respiration?

Substance 1 ....

Substance 2 ....

c) What two substances are produced by respiration?

Substance 1 ....

Substance 2 ....

Q4 *If 1g of glucose is burnt, it releases enough energy to light a 100W bulb for over 2½ minutes! Some of the energy released by respiration can be used to keep a steady body temperature in cold surroundings. In respiration, enzymes release the energy in small steps.*

What would happen if all the energy in cells was released in one go?

....

....

SECTION THREE — HUMAN BIOLOGY PART ONE

Questions on Respiration

Q5 The chemical equation for burning glucose is:

Glucose + oxygen $\longrightarrow$ carbon dioxide + water (+ energy transferred)

a) Write down one thing that is similar in respiration and burning.

....

b) Write down one thing that is different between respiration and burning.

....

Q6 *Houdini, the School hamster, certainly eats a lot — but is he respiring?*
The diagram below shows an experiment to see if Houdini is respiring.

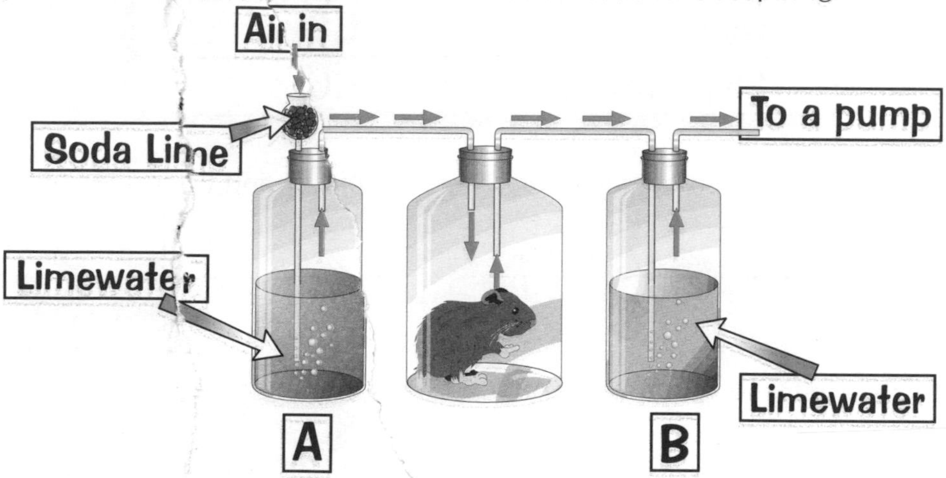

a) If Houdini really is respiring, which gases should he produce?

Gas 1 ....

Gas 2 ....

b) Which gas does limewater detect? ....

c) What does limewater do when it detects this gas? ....

d) The limewater in flask A stays clear, but in flask B it goes cloudy. What does this indicate?

....

e) After a while, some droplets of condensed water vapour appear on the inside of Houdini's

flask. Write down a possible reason for this.

....

....

Questions on Respiration

Q7 *The rate of oxygen uptake is a measure of the metabolic rate of the organism.* The table below shows the rate of oxygen uptake by different animals.

Animal	Uptake of Oxygen (cm^3 of O_2 / kg / min)
Mouse	26.0
Rat	13.8
Cat	10.5
Dog	5.2
Human	3.3
Horse	1.6
Elephant	1.0

a) What pattern can you see between the different animals and their rates of oxygen uptake?

....

....

b) Suggest a reason for the pattern in your answer to part a).

....

....

....

Q8 Paul wanted to show that leaf cells respire. He knew that water vapour is produced by respiration, so he set up the experiment shown on the right.

He used blue cobalt chloride paper to detect any water given off by the leaf. Blue cobalt chloride paper turns pink in water.

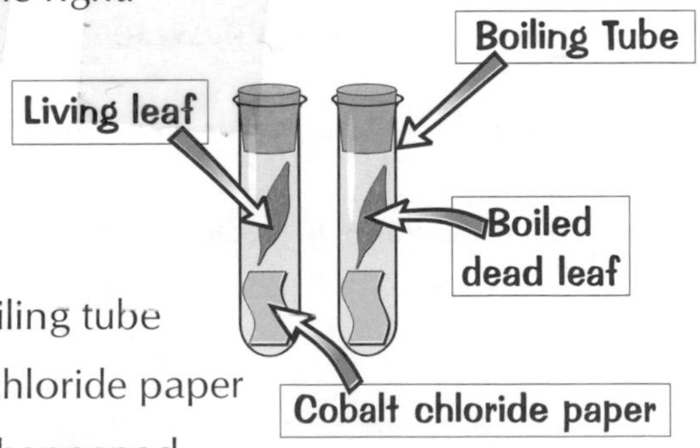

Paul only expected to detect water vapour in the boiling tube with the living leaf. To his surprise, the blue cobalt chloride paper turned pink in both boiling tubes. Suggest why this happened.

Boiling Tube

Living leaf

Boiled dead leaf

Cobalt chloride paper

....

....

....

Questions on Anaerobic Respiration

Q1 The word equation for _aerobic_ respiration is:

> glucose + oxygen $\longrightarrow$ carbon dioxide + water (+ energy transferred)

In _anaerobic_ respiration in humans, energy is released by converting glucose into lactic acid. No oxygen is needed for this to happen.

a) Write the word equation for anaerobic respiration in humans:

.... $\longrightarrow$ .... + ...

b) Aerobic respiration releases 16,000 J from 1g of glucose, and anaerobic respiration releases 833 J from 1g of glucose. Which process releases the most energy from glucose?

....

c) Write down one similarity, and one difference between aerobic and anaerobic respiration.

Similarity ....

Difference ....

d) Why are the two types of respiration named aerobic and anaerobic?

....

....

Q2 Complete the sentences below about anaerobic respiration using the words from this list:

cramp	energy	shortage	oxygen
lactic acid		poison	respiring

Anaerobic respiration in humans produces .... from glucose without

needing .... This means that when there is a .... of oxygen, cells

can carry on .... for a short time.

Anaerobic respiration releases .... as a waste. This is a mild ....

and can cause ....

Questions on Anaerobic Respiration

Q3   *David does a simple experiment to investigate respiration and muscle activity.*

He rapidly clenches and unclenches his fist, counting how many times he can do this before his hand feels like it's going to fall off. His results are shown in the table on the right.

Number of clenches	
hand lowered	hand raised
68	19

Circle the correct words in each of the <u>underlined</u> pairs in the sentences below:

a) At the start of the experiment, <u>aerobic</u> / <u>anaerobic</u> respiration was happening in his muscles.

b) At the end of the experiment, <u>aerobic</u> / <u>anaerobic</u> respiration was happening in his muscles.

c) During the experiment, <u>lactic acid</u> / <u>carbon dioxide</u> was made which caused cramp.

d) Why does it make a difference whether his hand is raised or lowered during the experiment?

....

....

Q4   Suggest why we sometimes feel a painful "stitch" in our sides when we have been running a lot.

....

....

Q5   The word equation for fermentation is:

glucose $\longrightarrow$ alcohol + carbon dioxide (+ energy transferred).

Circle the correct words in each of the <u>underlined</u> pairs in the sentences below:

a) Fermentation is an example of <u>aerobic</u> / <u>anaerobic</u> respiration.

b) Yeast is a microscopic <u>bacterium</u> / <u>fungus</u> that can produce <u>oxygen</u> / <u>carbon dioxide</u> and <u>water</u> / <u>alcohol</u> from glucose by fermentation.

Q6   *Animals do not use fermentation as a way of releasing energy from glucose.*

Suggest a reason why not.

....

....

Questions on Anaerobic Respiration

Q7 *The diagram on the right shows an experiment to show fermentation by yeast.*

a) What should be added to the yeast suspension to let fermentation start?

....

b) What change would you expect to see in the limewater?

....

....

Q8 Kathryn has entered a running race. The graph opposite shows the amount of *lactic acid* in her blood and her rate of oxygen uptake during the race.

The race takes place between the times marked A and B on the graph.

a) What type of respiration is most likely to be occurring when Kathryn is resting before the race?

Answer: .... respiration.

b) Kathryn's rate of oxygen uptake reaches a maximum during the race. Why can't she take up any more oxygen than this?

....

....

c) Why does the concentration of lactic acid in her blood increase during the race?

....

....

d) The shaded area on the graph is known as the oxygen debt. What is the oxygen debt?

....

....

....

Questions on The Nervous System

Q1   Circle the correct words in each of the underlined pairs in the sentences below:
The nervous system allows us to <u>react to</u> / <u>change</u> our surroundings.

The nervous system allows us to <u>improve</u> / <u>coordinate</u> our behaviour.

Q2 a) Put a tick in the box next to each correct sentence about the nervous system:

☐ Receptors are cells which can detect changes in the environment.
☐ A stimulus is a change in the environment.
☐ There are receptors in the ear which are sensitive to changes in position.
☐ Nerve impulses pass from the brain to the receptors.

b) The sentence without a tick is incorrect. Write down a correct version of it in the space below.

....

Q3   Match up the following sense organs with the receptors they contain.

| Organs | ⟹ | Receptors |

eyes have receptors

ears have receptors

tongue and nose have receptors

skin have receptors

that are sensitive to pressure and temperature

that are sensitive to light

that are sensitive to chemicals

that are sensitive to sound and changes in position

Q4   Complete the sentences below using the words from this list:

| see | skin | pressure | taste | nose | hear | balance |

The eye is the organ which allows us to .... The .... is the

organ which gives us the sense of touch by responding to changes in ....

The tongue gives us the sense of .... and the ....

allows us to smell things. The ears are important because they allow us to ....

and keep our ....

Q5   The diagram on the right shows the main features of the nervous system.

a) Name the parts of the nervous system labelled X, Y and Z.

X : ....   Y: ....

Z: ....

b) When parts X and Y are taken together, they have a name. What is this name?

Name of parts X and Y together: ....

c) In which direction can nerve impulses travel in the part labelled Y?
Circle the correct answer from the three choices below:

i) From the brain only   **ii)** To the brain only   **iii)** Both to and from the brain

SECTION THREE — HUMAN BIOLOGY PART ONE

Questions on The Nervous System

Q6 *When some grit gets in your eye, your eye begins to water. This is a reflex action. The grit irritates the eye, and is the stimulus. The eyes watering is the response.*

  a) Write down another example of a reflex action.

  ....

  b) Name the stimulus, and the response, in this reflex action.

  Stimulus .... Response ....

Q7 Circle the correct words from each underlined pair in the sentences below:

  A reflex action is <u>a conscious</u> / <u>an automatic</u> response. It is a response to a <u>stimulus</u> / <u>receptor</u>.

  Reflex actions happen very <u>quickly</u> / <u>slowly</u>. They <u>involve</u> / <u>do not involve</u> the <u>brain</u> / <u>Brian</u>.

  Reflex actions are <u>considered</u> / <u>emergency</u> reactions.

Q8 The diagram on the right shows a sensory neurone.

  Draw an arrow on the diagram to show the direction in which the nerve impulse travels.

Q9 The diagram on the right shows a motor neurone (effector neurone).

  Draw an arrow on the diagram to show the direction in which the nerve impulse travels.

Q10 Complete these sentences about neurones.

  Choose from the list of words below. You can use words more than once, if you need to.

receptor	effector	spinal cord

  a) Sensory neurones carry nerve impulses from the .... to the ....

  b) Motor neurones carry nerve impulses from the .... to the ....

Q11 *The spinal cord can be damaged from an accident or an illness. As a result, the person may be unable to feel anything below the damaged part of the spinal cord.*
Explain why this happens.

  ....

  ....

Q12 *The diagrams on the right show sections through a nerve and an electricity cable.*
Write down one similarity and one difference between a nerve and its nerve fibres (part of a neurone), and the cable.

  Nerve Fibre

  Similarity ....

  Difference ....

Questions on The Eye

Q1 *Look at the diagram below. It shows a section through an eye.*
— Label the different parts A to K, in the spaces provided.

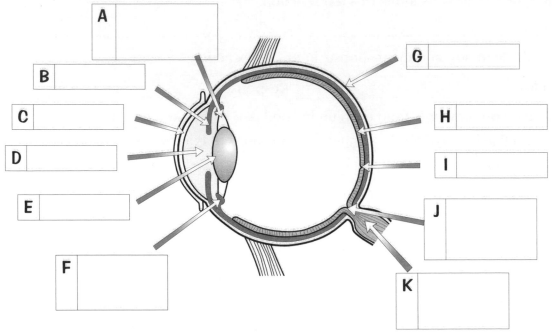

A

B

C

D

E

F

G

H

I

J

K

Q2 *The parts below are all involved in focusing light.* Match the "parts" to their correct "function".

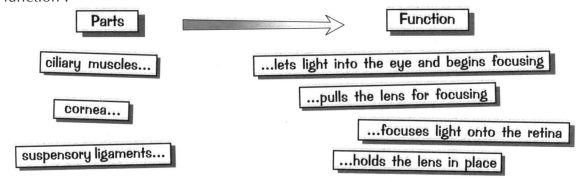

Parts → Function

ciliary muscles...

cornea...

suspensory ligaments...

...lets light into the eye and begins focusing

...pulls the lens for focusing

...focuses light onto the retina

...holds the lens in place

Q3 *The iris contains circular and radial muscles. These muscles control the diameter of the pupil.*

The diagrams on the right show the iris in two different light conditions.

a) What is the black circle in the centre?

....

b) Circle the correct <u>underlined</u> words in this sentence:

Muscle type A is <u>circular</u> / <u>radial</u> muscle and muscle type B is <u>circular</u> / <u>radial</u> muscle.

c) Which diagram, 1 or 2, shows the eye in bright light? Explain how you know this.

....

....

SECTION THREE — HUMAN BIOLOGY PART ONE

Questions on The Eye

Q4 a) Put a tick in the box next to each correct sentence about the parts of the eye:

☐ The cornea is a transparent region at the front of the sclera.

☐ The pupil controls the size of the iris.

☐ The retina contains receptor cells that are sensitive to light.

b) Write down a correct version of the sentence that is wrong in the space below.

....

Q5 Complete these sentences about the eye. Choose from the list of words below.

impulses	lens	cornea	retina	receptor	curved	optic

Light from an object goes through the .... into the eye. The

.... and the cornea (which is ....) focus an image on the

.... The retina has .... cells which send ....

to the brain though the .... nerve.

Q6 *The diagrams on the right show rays of light coming from an object on the left, and going through a fat lens or a thin lens.*

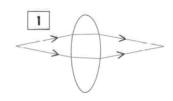 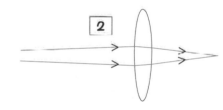

a) Which diagram shows light coming from a distant object? ....

b) In which diagram do the light rays bend the most, to join together on the right? ....

If a screen were placed where the rays come together on the right, an image of the object would be seen on the screen.

c) Circle the correct word from each of the <u>underlined</u> pairs in the sentences below.

1. Light from a distance object can be focused on the retina when the lens is <u>fat</u> / <u>thin</u>.

2. Light from a nearby object can be focused on the retina when the lens is <u>fat</u> / <u>thin</u>.

d) *The diagram below shows the cornea, lens and retina of the eye.*

Draw in two rays of light to show how light from the dog is focused on the retina — draw one ray from the top of the dog,

 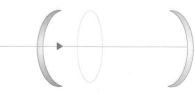

and one from the bottom. A middle ray (which does not bend) has been drawn in for you. (Remember that light is bent going through the cornea and the lens).

Questions on the Uses of Hormones

Q1 Complete the diagram below to show how hormones travel from a gland, causing a response in a target organ.

Choose from the list of words below:

stimulus	endocrine gland	hormone	bloodstream	response	target organ

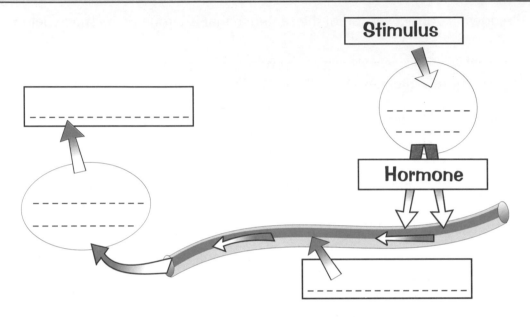

Stimulus

Hormone

Q2 *Hormones are important in controlling the level of sugar in the blood. One hormone reduces the amount of sugar in the blood, and the other hormone increases it.*
Study the diagram below and answer the questions.

a) Name the hormone in the diagram.

....

b) Where is this hormone made?

....

c) Name the target organ for this hormone.

....

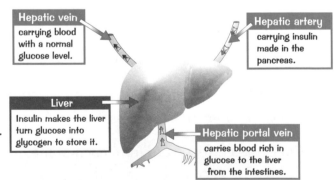

Hepatic vein carrying blood with a normal glucose level.

Hepatic artery carrying insulin made in the pancreas.

Liver Insulin makes the liver turn glucose into glycogen to store it.

Hepatic portal vein carries blood rich in glucose to the liver from the intestines.

d) Does this hormone cause the level of glucose in the blood to go up or down? ....

e) Use your answers to complete these sentences about the amount of sugar in blood:

A hormone called .... is made in the ....

This hormone is transported by the bloodstream to its target organ, which is the

.... Here, glucose is turned into .... which

.... the amount of sugar.

Questions on the Uses of Hormones

Q3 Complete the sentences below about hormones using the words from this list:

target	glands	processes	bloodstream	co-ordinated	chemicals

Many .... in the body are .... by hormones.

Hormones are .... They are produced by endocrine

....

Hormones are transported to their .... organs by the

....

Q4 Complete the diagram below to show how the level of sugar in the blood returns to normal after a meal rich in carbohydrates is eaten:

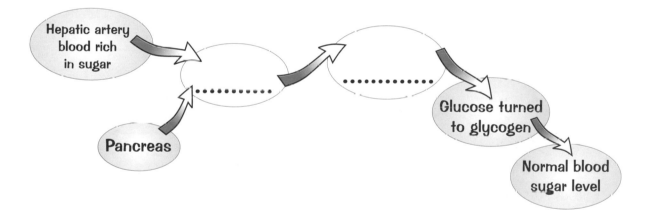

Q5 *Diabetes is a disease in which the pancreas does not produce enough insulin*

a) What will happen to the level of sugar in the blood if enough insulin is not produced?

....

....

b) Why do people with diabetes need to pay careful attention to their diet?

....

....

c) *Diabetes can be treated by injecting insulin into the bloodstream.* What will this do?

....

....

SECTION FOUR — HUMAN BIOLOGY PART TWO

Questions on the Uses of Hormones

Q6 *Glucagon is another hormone produced by the pancreas. It is also involved in controlling the level of sugar in blood. What does it do?*

....

....

Q7 *Hormones control many growth processes in our bodies. The graph below shows the variation in the relative rates of growth of the brain and reproductive organs, compared to the other organs of the body.*

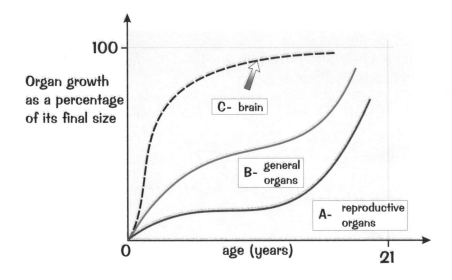

Study the graph. From the information in the graph, at what ages are hormones that cause increased growth likely to be active in:

a) The reproductive organs: Age ....

b) The general organs: Age ....

c) The brain: Age ....

Q8 *Two hormones are important in the sexual development of young people (adolescents).*

a) Which hormone co-ordinates the changes in boys as they mature?

....

b) Which hormone co-ordinates the changes in girls as they mature?

....

SECTION FOUR — HUMAN BIOLOGY PART TWO

Questions on Hormones and Fertility

Q1 *The hormones testosterone and oestrogen co-ordinate the changes in boys and girls as they grow and mature. The chart below shows the major changes that happen during adolescence. Some changes happen only to boys, some happen only to girls, and some happen to both.*

Match the changes to the correct gender (boys, girls, or both). One has been completed for you:

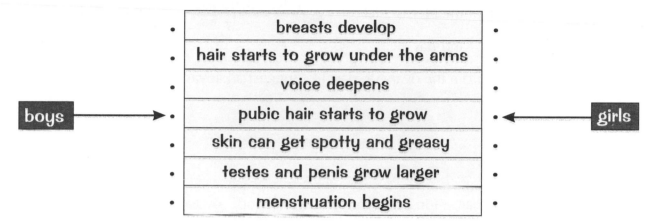

breasts develop	
hair starts to grow under the arms	
voice deepens	
boys → pubic hair starts to grow ← **girls**	
skin can get spotty and greasy	
testes and penis grow larger	
menstruation begins	

Q2 *The diagram below shows the female reproductive system.*

Complete the diagram by writing these labels in the correct boxes:

Fallopian tube (oviduct)	ovary	uterus (womb)	vagina

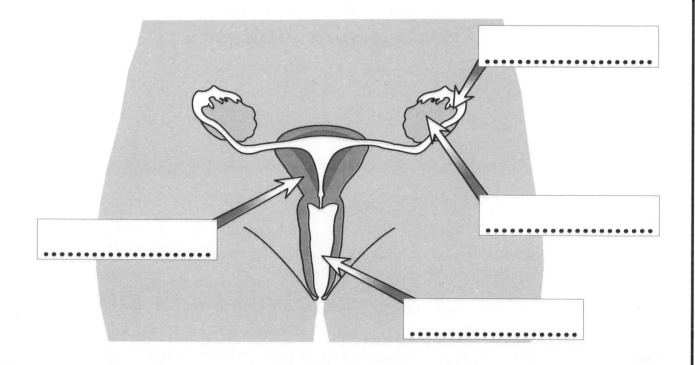

Questions on Hormones and Fertility

Q3 *The lining of a woman's uterus changes in thickness in a monthly cycle, ready to receive an egg.*

a) What is this monthly cycle called? ....

The diagram on the right shows these changes in thickness during a 28 day cycle. Study the diagram, then answer these questions:

Days 0   7   14   21   28

b) When is the lining of the uterus thickest?

Between day .... and day ....

c) An egg is released from the ovary on day 14. Suggest an advantage of releasing an egg then.

....

....

d) Circle the correct name for the monthly loss of blood: ovulation/menstruation/micrition.

Q4 Match the descriptions below to the correct term. One has been done for you.

Description	Term
Eggs are released from the organs called ●	● menstruation
The hormone that controls the uterus lining thickness is made in ●	● ovulation
The monthly loss of the uterus lining is called ●	
The monthly release of an egg is called ●	● the ovaries

Q5 Name a place where hormones are made that control the female reproductive system.

....

Q6 Write down two events in the menstrual cycle that are controlled by hormones.

a) ....   b) ....

Q7 *Women's fertility can be controlled using manufactured hormones.* Circle the correct word in each of the underlined pairs in the sentences below:

a) A woman's fertility increases / decreases if she is given hormones that stimulate egg release.

b) A woman's fertility increases / decreases if she is given hormones that prevent egg release.

SECTION FOUR — HUMAN BIOLOGY PART TWO

Questions on Hormones and Fertility

Q8 Write down one advantage of using manufactured hormones to control fertility in women, and one disadvantage of doing this.

Advantage: ....

....

Disadvantage: ....

....

Q9 Solve the Hormones Wordsearch!

Words to find:

bloodstream	chemicals	endocrine	gland	glucagon
hormone	insulin	liver		oestrogen
ovaries	pancreas	pituitary	testosterone	uterus

Questions on Disease in Humans

Q1 *The two main types of microbes that can cause disease are bacteria and viruses.* Write down the name of each type of microbe shown in the pictures on the right. (the pictures are not drawn to scale).

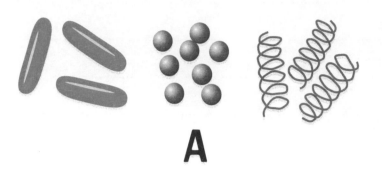

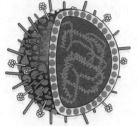

A ....

B ....

Q2 *Bacteria and viruses are very different from each other. Their main features are shown below.*

| have a cell wall |
| reproduce only in living cells |
| about $1/10,000^{th}$ mm in size |

| have a protein coat |
| have cytoplasm and a membrane |
| about $1/1000^{th}$ mm in size |

Complete the table below by writing each feature in the correct column. One feature of each has already been done for you.

Bacteria	Viruses
about $1/1000^{th}$ mm in size	about $1/10,000^{th}$ mm in size

Q3 Which type of microbe is the largest, bacteria or viruses? ....

Questions on Disease in Humans

Q4   *Microbes must get inside our bodies before they can cause disease.*
Write down three ways that microbes might get into our bodies.

a)   ....

b)   ....

c)   ....

Q5   *You are more likely to get a disease if large numbers of microbes get into your body.*

Put a tick ✓ in the box ☐ next to each correct sentence:

☐   Large numbers of bacteria can get into your body through a cut.

☐   You are less likely to get a disease in crowded places.

☐   You are more likely to get a disease in unhygienic conditions.

Q6   *Bacteria can reproduce more rapidly in certain conditions.*

a)   Why is the body often an ideal place for bacteria to grow in?

....

....

b)   Why can it be unsafe to eat food that has been left out of the refrigerator for too long?

....

....

Q7   Complete the table below to show which type of microbe (bacteria or virus) causes each disease. One line has been completed for you.

Disease	Type of microbe (bacteria or virus)
Common cold	
Measles	
Cholera	
Polio	Virus
Whooping Cough	

Questions on Disease in Humans

Q8 Write down two ways in which bacteria or viruses can be passed from one person to another.

a) ....

....

b) ....

....

Q9 *When bacteria and viruses grow in our bodies, they can produce chemicals called toxins.* Write down another name for these chemicals.

Name: ....

Q10 *When viruses reproduce in a cell, they break out of the cell in large numbers and infect other cells.* Circle the correct words from each of the <u>underlined</u> pairs in the sentences below:

Viruses escape from an infected cell through the cell's *nucleus* / *membrane*.

When viruses escape from an infected cell, they <u>*do*</u> / <u>*do not*</u> damage the cell.

Viruses <u>*do*</u> / <u>*do not*</u> need to reproduce inside living cells.

Q11 Complete the sentences below about microbes and disease using the words from this list:

genes   protein   microbes   toxins   rapidly   smaller   nucleus

Diseases can be caused when .... get into the body. Bacteria

and viruses reproduce .... inside the body. They produce

.... which make us feel ill. Viruses are ....

than bacteria, and consist of a .... coat with a few genes inside.

Bacteria have .... but they are not in a ....

Q12 *In Japan, people with a cold often wear a mask over their mouth and nose when they go outside.*

Suggest a reason why they do this. ....

Questions on Fighting Disease

Q1 *Microbes must get into the body before they can cause disease.*

Our bodies have several natural defences that can stop microbes getting in.

Match the natural defence to the correct part of the body:

natural defence	⟶	part of the body

hydrochloric acid is produced to kill microbes		skin
acts as a barrier to microbes		stomach
a sticky liquid is produced to trap microbes		blood
clots are produced to seal cuts		breathing organs

Q2 *Cells in the blood can defend the body against microbes if they manage to get past the natural defences. The diagrams on the right show cells that are found in blood.* Write down the name of each type of cell in the spaces. Choose from these labels:

....

....

red cell   white cell

Q3 *White cells help to defend the body against microbes that cause disease.*

What do the red cells do?

....

....

Q4 Complete the sentences below using the words from the box:

phagocytes	toxins	ingest	antibodies	antitoxins	microbes

White cells can produce .... which destroy particular

.... They also produce .... which counteract

poisons called .... Special white cells called ....

can .... microbes and so destroy them.

Questions on Fighting Disease

Q5 *At each stage in getting a disease caused by a microbe, the body has defences.*
For each of the stages below, write down an example of the body's defence against microbes:

Bacteria getting into a cut: ....

....

Bacteria producing toxins: ....

....

Bacteria being breathed in: ....

....

Q6 Look at the diagram on
the right, then write down
below how each of the
parts **A** to **D** can protect
the body against
microbes.

A ....

....

B ....

....

C ....

....

D ....

....

SECTION FOUR — HUMAN BIOLOGY PART TWO

Questions on Fighting Disease

Q7   *In an experiment, somebody was injected with microbes. After 20 days they had produced 1 unit of antibody. After a few months, they were injected again with the same type of microbe. This time, they produced 2.5 units of antibody after 17 days.*

a)   Circle the correct words in the underlined pairs in the sentence below:

When you are exposed to a microbe for the second time, the

production of antibodies is <u>slower</u> / <u>faster</u> than the first time, and

<u>more</u> / <u>less</u> antibody is produced than the first time.

b)   *When you are vaccinated against a microbe that causes disease, you are usually injected with dead or damaged microbes, or parts of the microbe.* Explain how vaccinations protect you from microbes that cause disease.

....

....

....

Q8   Use the list of infectious diseases in the box on the right to complete the table.

diphtheria   measles   tetanus   rubella   mumps   whooping cough (pertussis)

MMR vaccine protects against	DPT vaccine protects against

Q9   Suggest reasons for the following precautions:

a)   Putting a sticking plaster over a cut: ....

....

b)   Sneezing into a hankie when you have a cold: ....

....

c)   Washing your hands after going to the toilet: ....

....

Questions on Drugs

Q1 a) Match the substances below to the correct descriptions.

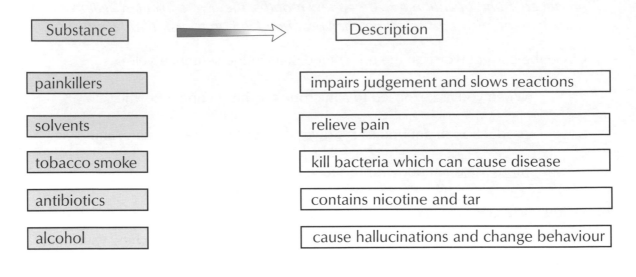

| Substance | ⟹ | Description |

painkillers

solvents

tobacco smoke

antibiotics

alcohol

impairs judgement and slows reactions

relieve pain

kill bacteria which can cause disease

contains nicotine and tar

cause hallucinations and change behaviour

b) Which two substances in part a) are often prescribed by doctors to help people?

....

c) Choose one of the substances in part b). Give one reason why a doctor would give it to you.

....

Q2 a) Write the names of each of the organs drawn below in the correct boxes.

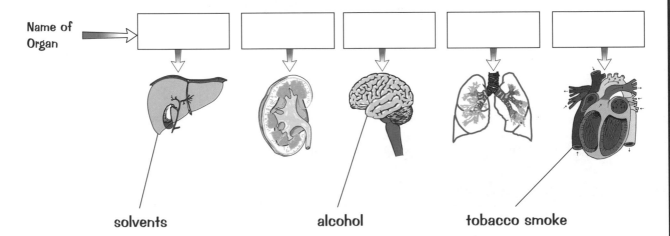

Name of Organ

solvents   alcohol   tobacco smoke

b) Draw lines to match the drugs to the organs they can damage. At least two lines should come from each drug. Three lines have been drawn already to get you started.

Q3   In the sentence below, circle the correct words in each of the underlined pairs.

Penicillin / paracetamol is an antibiotic, and aspirin / vancomycin is a painkiller.

SECTION FOUR — HUMAN BIOLOGY PART TWO

Questions on Drugs

Q4 Complete the sentences below about drugs using the words from this list:

addicted	processes	chemicals	ill	helpful	withdrawal

Drugs are .... which change the way the body works.

Some are .... to .... people, but

others change the chemical .... in people's bodies.

These changes can make people .... to them and suffer

from .... symptoms if they stop taking the drug.

Q5 a) Put a tick in the box next to each of the correct sentences about alcohol:

☐ Alcohol speeds up reactions and can lead to lack of self-control.

☐ Too much alcohol can lead to unconsciousness and coma.

☐ Alcohol can cause damage to liver and brain cells.

Q6 Study the diagram below, then answer the questions. One unit of alcohol is 10cm³ of alcohol.

a) How many units are there in ½ pint of beer?

.... Units.

b) How many units are there in a double measure of spirits?

.... Units.

½pint of beer contains approx. 10cm³ of alcohol = glass of wine = glass of sherry = single measure of spirits

c) *A person at a party drinks a pint of beer, 3 glasses of wine, and two double whiskies (a spirit).* How many units of alcohol has he drunk? Show your working out.

....

....

d) Why would it be unsafe for the person in part c) to drive home after the party?

....

....

Questions on Drugs

Q7 *The diagrams on the right show the alveoli of a normal lung, and those of a lung of someone suffering from emphysema (a lung disease).*

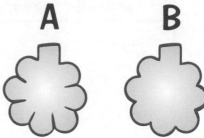

a) Which diagram (**A** or **B**) shows alveoli from a

normal lung? ....

b) Suggest why emphysema makes breathing difficult.

....

....

Q8 Circle the correct words in each of the underlined pairs in these sentences about tobacco smoke:

1) <u>Tar</u> / <u>nicotine</u> is the substance in tobacco smoke that can cause lung cancer.

2) The substance in tobacco smoke that causes addiction is <u>carbon monoxide</u> / <u>nicotine</u>.

Q9 *The table below shows the effects on the body of three common drugs.*

Complete the table using the words in the box. Some words can be used more than once. Put a tick in the last row if the substance is addictive.

Liver	Heart	Kidneys	Hallucinations
Slows reactions		Emphysema	Brain

	alcohol	tobacco	solvents
organs damaged	Brain and	Lungs and	Liver
effect on the body		Lung cancer and	
addictive?			

Questions on Homeostasis

Q1 *Water is a substance that must be kept at a constant level in the body for us to stay healthy.*

The table below shows the input and output of water by the body in a day.

Water going in (cm³)		Water going out (cm³)	
Food and drink	1850	Breathing	400
Respiration	(a)	Sweating	600
		Urine	1050
		Faeces	150
Total	2200	Total	(b)

a) Work out the amount of water going in by respiration in a day. Show your working.

....

....

b) Work out the total amount of water going out of the body in a day. Show your working.

....

....

c) Compare the total amount of water going into the body with your answer to part (b). What do you notice?

....

....

d) Using the information in the table, how is most water lost from the body?

....

....

e) What might happen if the amount of water going in was not the same as the amount going out?

....

....

....

Questions on Homeostasis

Q2 *The graph below shows the results of an experiment into the effects on the body of increasing the air temperature. The squares show the volume of urine produced per hour. The circles show the volume of sweat produced per hour.*

a) Circle the correct words in each underlined pair:

As the temperature goes up, the volume of

urine produced goes <u>up</u> / <u>down</u>, and the

volume of sweat produced goes <u>up</u> / <u>down</u>.

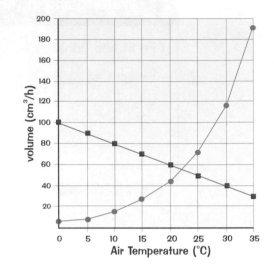

b) At which temperature is the volume of urine produced the same as the volume of sweat?

Temperature = ... °C

c) Why do we feel more thirsty in hot weather?

....

....

Q3 Match the method of water loss to the correct organ in the body:

Method of water loss		Organ
water is lost by sweating through the		kidneys
water is lost by breathing using the		skin
water is lost as urine made in the		lungs

Q4 *In an experiment, 10 members of a class took their temperatures. Their results are shown below:*

Body temperature in °C
36.7 36.8 37.1 36.9 36.9 37.0 37.3 36.8 37.2 37.1

a) Work out the average body temperature for these 10 students. Show your working out.

.... °C

b) What is normal human body temperature? .... °C

Questions on Homeostasis

Q5 *For us to stay healthy, the temperature of the body must be maintained at the temperature that enzymes work best.*
The table below shows how the temperature of a human body and a reptile's body changes during the day in a hot climate.

Time	4 a.m	8 a.m	12 noon	4 p.m	8 p.m	midnight
Air Temperature (°C)	10	22	39	39	30	8
Human body temperature (°C)	37	37	37	37	37	37
Reptile body temperature (°C)	7	19	10	10	19	7

a) Between which times is the air temperature highest? Between .... and ....

b) The reptile goes underground when the air temperature is highest. Why does it do this?

....

c) What happens to the human's body temperature during the day? ....

d) Circle the correct words in each of the underlined pairs in the sentences below:

1. Reptiles can / cannot use energy from respiration to maintain their body temperature.

2. Humans can / cannot use energy from respiration to maintain their body temperature.

3. Humans maintain their body temperature by sweating when the air temperature gets

low / high.

e) *If the body temperature falls too far, we get sleepy and cannot move easily. This is called hypothermia. Suggest why old people may be at particular risk of hypothermia in winter.*

....

....

Q6 *The amount of sugar in the blood must be kept at a constant level for us to stay healthy.*

a) Name the two hormones involved in keeping the blood sugar level constant.

Hormone 1 ....   Hormone 2 ....

b) *In a certain disease, one of these hormones is only produced in small amounts, and the blood sugar level might rise to fatal levels. Name the disease and the hormone involved.*

Name of disease ....   Name of hormone ....

Questions on Skin

Q1 *If we get embarrassed or too hot, our skin goes red. This is because the capillaries in the skin get wider and let more blood through.*

Circle the correct words in the <u>underlined</u> pairs in the sentences below about the skin:

a) When the capillaries get wider, this is called <u>vasoconstriction</u> / <u>vasodilation</u>.

b) When we get cold, <u>less</u> / <u>more</u> blood goes through our skin, and our skin looks <u>blue</u> / <u>red</u>.

c) When we get cold, our hairs <u>stand up</u> / <u>lie down</u> to trap a layer of warm air near the skin.

Q2 Complete the flow chart to show how the skin helps us maintain a constant body temperature. Use the words in the box below.

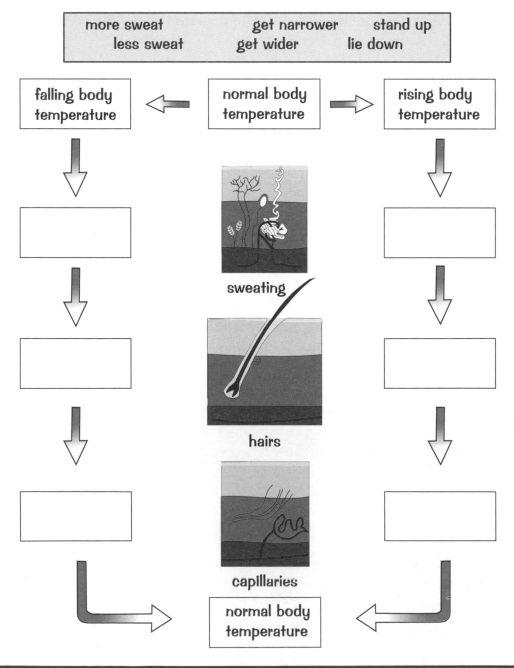

Questions on Skin

Q3 Complete the sentences below about the skin, using the words from the box:

vasoconstriction	lie down	capillaries	hairs	blood	narrower

When the body gets too cold, the .... in our skin get

.... and let less .... through. This is called

.... When we get too hot, the .... on

our skin .... to let heat escape from the skin.

Q4 *The skin is the largest organ of the body. It plays important roles in keeping the body free from disease and protecting our internal organs.*

a) How does the skin protect us from disease?

....

....

b) Why is the skin waterproof?

....

....

Q5 *We sweat to help maintain a constant body temperature. Sweat contains water and salts.*

a) Put a tick in the box next to each correct sentence:

☐ Water also leaves the body in urine.

☐ Water also leaves the body through the lungs when we breathe in.

☐ Salts also leave the body in urine.

b) *There should be only one box without a tick.* Write down a correct version of this sentence in the space below.

....

....

Questions on Kidneys

Q1 *The diagram on the right shows the parts of the excretory system. Six parts are labelled, A to F.*

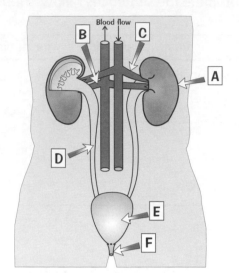

a) Complete the table below by filling in the names of the labelled parts.

Label	Name of part
A	
B	
C	
D	
E	
F	

b) Match the parts to the correct functions (the diagram may help you do this). One has been for you already.

Parts ⟶ Functions

Parts	Functions
bladder	filtration and reabsorption
kidneys	supplies blood to the kidney
renal arteries	transport of urine out of the body
renal veins	storage of urine
ureters	takes blood away from the kidneys
urethra	transport of urine to the bladder

SECTION FOUR — HUMAN BIOLOGY PART TWO

Questions on Kidneys

Q2 a) Put a tick in the box next to each correct sentence about the excretory system:

☐	The kidneys remove excess water from the bloodstream.
☐	Urea is produced by the kidneys from the breakdown of excess amino acids.
☐	Urea is removed by the kidneys, and stored temporarily in urine in the bladder.

b) *There should be only one box without a tick.* Write down a correct version of this sentence in the space below.

....

Q3 Complete the sentences below about the excretory system using the words from this list:

liver	sweat	bladder	veins	balance	poison
arteries	urine	kidneys	urethra	ions	ureters

The renal .... supply blood to the kidneys, and the renal

.... take blood away from the kidneys. The .... remove

urea from the body. This is a .... that is produced in the

.... is transported from the kidneys to the bladder

through two .... Urine is stored in the .... before

being lost from the body through the ....

The kidneys also remove excess water and .... from the body. These can

be lost in ...., but the kidneys maintain the correct .... of

these substances.

Q4 Suggest two problems that people with damaged kidneys may face.

....

....

....

Questions on the Variation in Plants and Animals

Q1 *Individual animals and plants of the same species are usually not identical.
They have different characteristics from each other, and show variation.*
Match the *description* to the correct *meaning*:

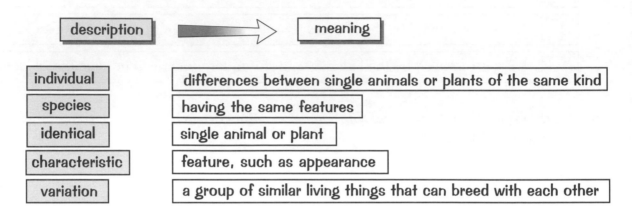

| description | | meaning |

individual	differences between single animals or plants of the same kind
species	having the same features
identical	single animal or plant
characteristic	feature, such as appearance
variation	a group of similar living things that can breed with each other

Q2 *There are two types of variation.
— continuous variation, and
discontinuous variation.*

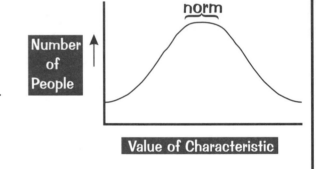

norm

Number
of
People

Value of Characteristic

a) Which type of variation is shown in the graph?

....

b) *Some people have earlobes, and some do not.
A class surveyed their ears to see how many
students had earlobes and how many did not.*

Draw labelled bars in the blank graph on the right
to show the sort of results the students might
have obtained.

Number
of
People

c) Which type of variation is shown by the earlobe
survey?

....

Value of Characteristic

Q3 Humans show variation in many of their characteristics. The box below shows six of these
characteristics. Three of them show *continuous* variation, and three of them show
discontinuous variation. Complete the table on the right using these characteristics.

weight
ability to roll tongue
lobed ears
height
intelligence
sex (gender)

continuous variation	discontinuous variation

Questions on the Variation in Plants and Animals

Q4 People belong to one of four main blood groups, A, B, AB, or O.

Complete the sentences below about blood groups using the words from this list:

group	discontinuous	categories	four	variation

There are .... main blood groups. The .... in these blood

groups is .... This is because there are distinct .... of

blood ....

Q5 Animals and plants look similar to their parents because of information passed onto them by their parents. Genes carry this information. Variation between individuals can be due to differences in the genes they have inherited, to differences in the conditions around them, or both.

Complete the sentences below by circling the correct word in each of the brackets.

Differences in the (**genes / conditions**) produce variation due to genetic causes.

Variation caused by the (**environment / habitat**) is due to differences in conditions.

A mixture of genetic and environmental differences (**can / cannot**) cause variation.

Q6 Identical twins have the same genes and are said to be genetically identical.

The table below shows the characteristics of four people, code-named M, Q, X, and Z.

Characteristic	M	Q	X	Z
They have a sun tan	✓	✓		
They are male	✓	✓	✓	
They are female				✓
They can roll their tongue	✓		✓	
Natural hair colour is brown	✓	✓	✓	✓
They have bleached white hair			✓	✓
They have brown eyes	✓	✓	✓	

a) Which people are male?

Code-names: ....

b) Who can roll their tongue and has a sun tan? Code-name: ....

c) Which two features are caused by differences in the environment?

1 .... 2 ....

d) Which two people must be the identical twins? Code-names: ....

Questions on the Variation in Plants and Animals

Q7 When Ayesha looked at the ivy plant growing up the tree in her back garden, she was surprised by how much the size and colour of the leaves varied.

a) What kind of variation is this, genetic or environmental? ....

b) All mature ivy leaves have the same shape.

Is leaf shape determined genetically or environmentally? ....

c) Is the size of the leaves a continuous or discontinuous variation?

....

Q8 Azra took geranium cuttings from one of the plants in her garden and gave half of them to her friend Andrew. Each grew their cuttings in their own gardens and a year later compared the growth of the plants and were amazed to see how differently the geraniums had grown.

The table shows what each set of plants looked like.

	Azra's plants	Andrew's plants
Leaves	Dark green, no spots	Pale green, brown spots
Stems	Tall and thick	Short and thin
Flowers	Large	Small

a) Suggest two things that could affect the appearance of the geranium plants.

1 ....

2 ....

b) Do you think that the differences in their plants are due to _environmental_ variations or

genetic variations? ....

c) Give one reason for your answer to part b).

....

....

....

d) Circle the correct words in each of the brackets to complete the sentences below:

"**All the flowers were orange**" — This is due to (**environmental / genetic**) causes.

"**The flowers were lots of different shades**" — This is (**continuous / discontinuous**) variation.

"**The plants are all of different heights**" — This is (**continuous / discontinuous**) variation

and is due to (**environmental / genetic**) causes.

Questions on Genes, Chromosomes and DNA

Q1   *Read the information in the box, then answer the questions.*

> DNA is a chemical found in the nucleus of cells.
>
> DNA is very long, so it is usually folded up into shapes called chromosomes to fit into the nucleus.
>
> A gene is a section of DNA which has the information needed to control a particular characteristic.

a) Where do you find DNA? ....

b) Why is DNA made into chromosomes?

....

c) What do we call a section of DNA
that controls a particular characteristic? ....

d) Is the diagram on the right an *animal* cell
or a *plant* cell?

....

e) Where in the cell would you
find the genes?

....

nucleus

cytoplasm

cell membrane

Q2   Put these structures into order, from smallest to largest:

| nucleus | gene | chromosome | cell |

.... ⇒ .... ⇒ .... ⇒ ....

Smallest   **Largest**

Q3   *The diagram on the right shows a typical chromosome.*

a) Put a tick ✓ in the box ☐ next to each correct
sentence about chromosomes:

☐ The name of the chemical in chromosomes is DNA.

☐ Genes contain lots of chromosomes.

☐ Chromosomes are found in the nucleus of the cell.

b) The sentence without a tick is incorrect. Write down a correct version of it in the space below.

....

SECTION FIVE — GENETICS AND EVOLUTION

96

Questions on Genes, Chromosomes and DNA

Q4 *An experiment was done with two fertilised frog eggs. The eggs came from completely different parents. The nucleus of egg A was put into egg B, and the nucleus of egg B was removed (see the diagram on the right).*

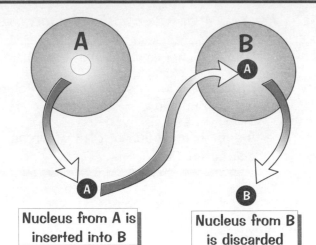

Nucleus from A is inserted into B

Nucleus from B is discarded

a) Egg A did not grow into a frog. Why not?

....

....

b) Egg B grew into a frog, but it looked like the parents of egg A, not the parents of egg B. Why was this?

....

Q5 *The diagrams below show the chromosomes in each body cell of a man and a woman.*

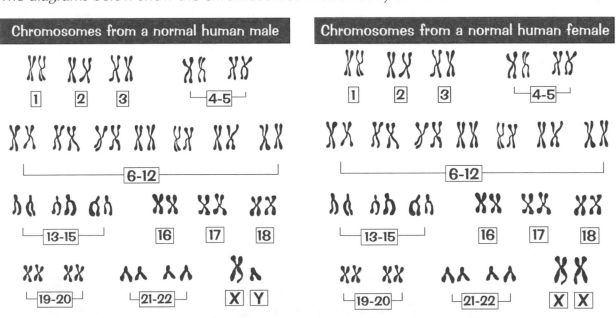

a) The chromosomes are found in pairs. How many pairs of chromosomes are there in each cell?
Number of pairs of chromosomes: ....

b) How many chromosomes are there altogether in each human body cell? ....

c) What is the difference between the two sets of chromosomes?

....

SECTION FIVE — GENETICS AND EVOLUTION

Questions on Genes, Chromosomes and DNA

Q6 a) Put a tick ✓ in the box ☐ next to each correct sentence about chromosomes:

    ☐   Chromosomes are found in pairs in body cells.

    ☐   Men have one X chromosome and one Y chromosome.

    ☐   The X chromosome is the chromosome needed for a baby to develop into a boy.

b) The sentence without a tick is incorrect. Write down a correct version of it in the space below.

....

....

Q7 *Melanin is the coloured substance in skin. The flow chart shows how melanin is made from a starting substance X. Enzymes are needed to turn substance X into substance Y, and then into melanin. Genes carry the information needed to make these enzymes.*

| Substance X | Enzyme A → | Substance Y | Enzyme B → | Melanin |

a) Some people *do not* have the gene to make substance X, but they can make substance Y.

Will they be able to make melanin? ....

b) Someone has the gene for enzyme A, but *not* the one for enzyme B.

Will they be able to make melanin? ....

Q8 *Haemophilia is a disease, only present in males, where an important protein cannot be made and consequently a sufferer's blood won't clot.*

a) What must be defective for the disease to occur?

....

b) On which chromosome does this defect occur?

....

c) Say whether the following sentences are true (**T**) or false (**F**) by circling the appropriate letter.

Females can suffer from haemophilia	(T / F)
Females can be carriers of haemophilia	(T / F)
Small cuts and knocks aren't particularly dangerous to haemophiliacs	(T / F)
There is no treatment for sufferers	(T / F)
Sufferers can be treated by regular injections of the clotting factor — Factor 8	(T / F)

Questions on Asexual Reproduction

Q1   *There are two types of reproduction, asexual reproduction and sexual reproduction.*
Complete the table below with the sentences in the box to show the differences between
asexual and sexual reproduction.

> Male and female sex cells join.
> Offspring are not genetically identical to parents.
> No joining of cells needed.
> Two parents are needed
> Offspring are genetically identical to parent.
> Only one parent is needed.

Asexual reproduction	Sexual reproduction

Q2   *Genetically identical individuals are called
clones. Gardeners can produce clones by
taking "cuttings" from one plant. If they are kept
in a damp atmosphere or in moist compost, the
cuttings eventually grow roots and become a
new plant (see diagram).*

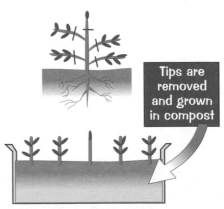

Tips are removed and grown in compost

a) Complete the following sentence:

Clones are .... **organisms.**

b) What type of reproduction is involved in this method?

....

c) Why are the new plants called *clones?*

....

d) Why would a gardener want to take cuttings from a plant that produces prize-winning
flowers?

....

Questions on Asexual Reproduction

Q3 *Unlike humans, many plants reproduce asexually.*

a) Give *three* examples of plants which reproduce asexually.

Example 1 ....

Example 2 ....

Example 3 ....

b) For one of the examples above say how the plant actually carries out asexual reproduction.

....

....

Strawberry plants can reproduce in two ways.
They can use flowers, and they can also use runners.

c) Put a tick ✓ in the box ☐ next to each correct sentence about reproduction in strawberry plants:

☐ Asexual reproduction involves runners.

☐ Flowers are needed for strawberry fruits to form.

☐ Seeds produce new plants that are genetically identical to each other.

d) The sentence without a tick is incorrect.
Write down a correct version of it in the space below.

....

Q4 *Bacteria can reproduce asexually by splitting in two. In good conditions, they can do this every 20 minutes. After 24 hours, this could produce nearly 5,000 billion billion offspring!*
Circle the correct answers in questions a), b) and c).
Starting with one bacterium:

a) After 20 minutes there would be 2 / 3 / 4 bacteria.

b) After 40 minutes there would be 3 / 4 / 8 bacteria.

c) After 60 minutes there would be 4 / 6 / 8 / 12 bacteria.

d) Complete the following passage about asexual reproduction using the words or phrases in the box below. You can use the word or phrases once, more than once or not at all.

all completely different   two   clones   exactly the same   one
For an organism to reproduce asexually, ... parent is needed. The offspring produced by this type of reproduction have genes which are .... as the parent. They are said to be .... of each other.

Questions on Sexual Reproduction

Q1 a) Complete the following sentences about sexual reproduction by circling the correct word in each of the brackets.

Sex cells are called (**gametes** / **genes**).

Male sex cells are called (**testes** / **sperm**). Female sex cells are called (**ova** / **ovaries**).

When sex cells join together this is called (**pollination** / **fertilisation**). The chromosomes (**pair up** / **divide in two**) and a (**foetus** / **zygote**) is formed.

b) Complete the diagram below to show what the chromosomes are like in the fertilised egg.

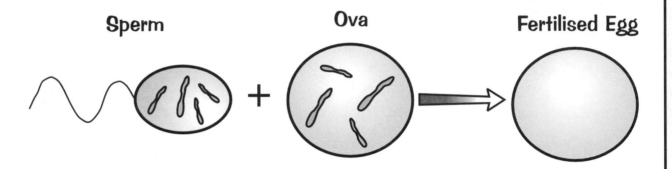

Sperm   **Ova**   **Fertilised Egg**

c) Do you think that in this form of reproduction, genetic information is inherited from _one_ parent or _both_ parents? ....

d) Complete the following sentence by circling the correct word in the brackets:

Offspring produced by sexual reproduction are genetically (**identical** / **different**) to their parents

Q2 In the diagrams below, ●— represents a sperm, ○ represents an egg, and ● the zygote.

A   C

B   D

a) Which of the diagrams shows how _identical twins_ can be formed? Diagram ....

b) Which of the diagrams shows how _non-identical twins_ can be formed? Diagram ....

Questions on Sexual Reproduction

Q3   *The diagram below shows part of the reproductive organs of a flowering plant.*

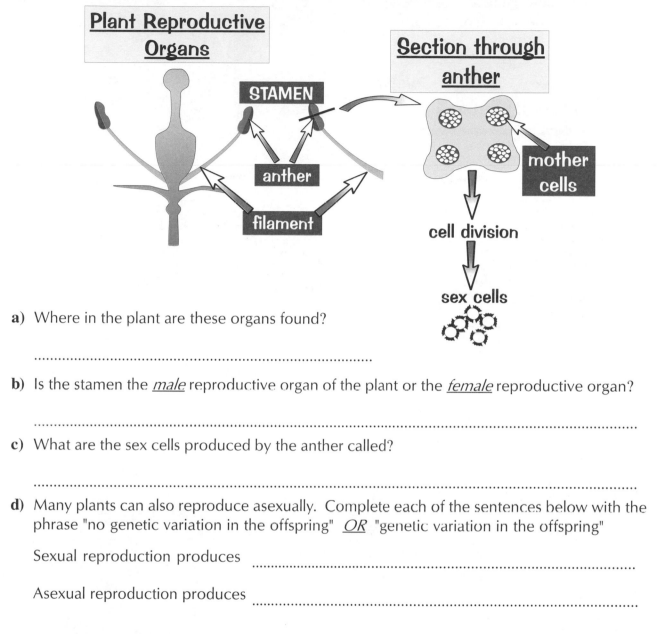

a) Where in the plant are these organs found?

....

b) Is the stamen the *male* reproductive organ of the plant or the *female* reproductive organ?

....

c) What are the sex cells produced by the anther called?

....

d) Many plants can also reproduce asexually. Complete each of the sentences below with the phrase "no genetic variation in the offspring" *OR* "genetic variation in the offspring"

Sexual reproduction produces ....

Asexual reproduction produces ....

Q4   Complete the sentences below about reproduction using the words from this list:

gametes	asexual	parent	zygote	sexual	offspring	identical	variation

.... reproduction needs just one parent. The offspring are genetically

.... to each other and to the .... In ....

reproduction, two parents are needed, each producing .... which join

together to form a .... The .... have a mixture of the parents'

genetic information and show more .... than offspring produced asexually.

Questions on Reproduction in Humans

Q1 The diagram on the right shows the female reproductive system. Use the words in the box below to label the diagram correctly.

> cervix   ovary   vagina
> oviduct   uterus

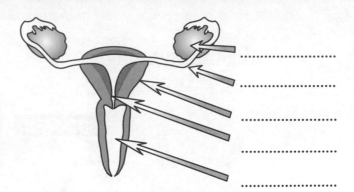

....

....

....

....

....

Q2 Match the parts of the female reproductive system to their correct description:

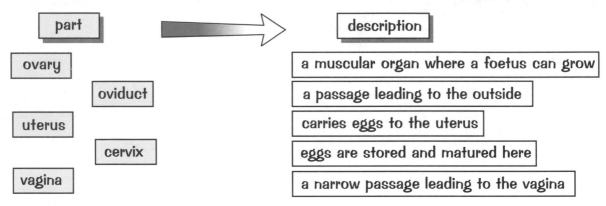

part		description

ovary

oviduct

uterus

cervix

vagina

a muscular organ where a foetus can grow

a passage leading to the outside

carries eggs to the uterus

eggs are stored and matured here

a narrow passage leading to the vagina

Q3 The diagram shows the male reproductive system. Use the words in the box below to label the diagram.

> penis   scrotum   testis
> urethra   sperm duct

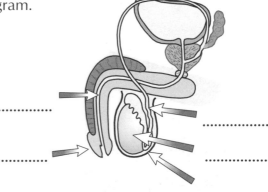

....

....

....

....

....

Q4 Match the parts of the male reproductive system to their correct description:

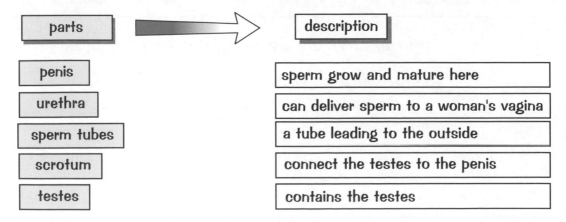

parts		description

penis

urethra

sperm tubes

scrotum

testes

sperm grow and mature here

can deliver sperm to a woman's vagina

a tube leading to the outside

connect the testes to the penis

contains the testes

SECTION FIVE — GENETICS AND EVOLUTION

Questions on Reproduction in Humans

Q5 *The charts below show what happens in the menstrual cycle when a woman does not become pregnant.*

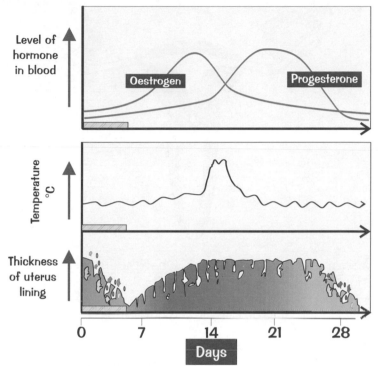

Study the charts, then circle the correct word in each bracket :

a) Between day 0 and day 5, the lining of the uterus (**builds up / breaks down**).

b) When the lining of the uterus breaks down, it is called (**implantation / menstruation**).

c) An egg is released around day 14. Body temperature is (**highest / lowest**) then.

d) As the level of oestrogen increases, the lining of the uterus gets (**thinner / thicker**).

e) After an egg is released, the level of (**oestrogen / progesterone**) reaches a maximum.

f) As the level of progesterone decreases, the lining of the uterus gets (**thinner / thicker**).

Q6 Complete the sentences below about reproduction using the words from the list:

fertilised	breaks	down	ovary	uterus	vagina	oviduct	thicker

A mature egg passes from the .... along the .... to the uterus.

The lining of the .... becomes .... ready to receive the egg if it

is .... If the egg is not fertilised, the lining ....

.... and is lost through the ....

Questions on Reproduction in Humans

Q7 *The diagram below shows the female reproductive system.*

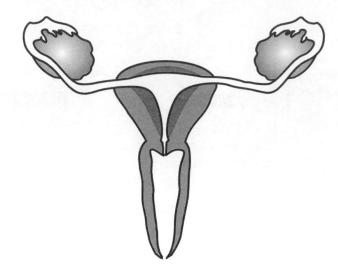

a) Draw a labelling line on the diagram to show where sperm is likely to be left during sexual intercourse. Label it as A.

b) Draw a labelling line on the diagram to show where an egg is likely to be fertilised by a sperm. Label it as B.

c) Draw a labelling line on the diagram to show where a fertilised egg is likely to implant and grow. Label it as C.

d) Draw a labelling line on the diagram to show where a baby leaves the mother. Label it as D.

Q8 Circle the correct words in each brackets to complete the sentences below:

a) The male gamete is called the (**egg / sperm**). It is made in the (**testes / ovary**).

b) The female gamete is called the (**egg / sperm**). It is made in the (**testes / ovary**).

c) The fertilised egg is called the (**foetus / zygote**). It grows to form the (**foetus / zygote**).

Q9 Complete the sentences below about reproduction using the words from this list:

urea	oxygen	embryo	umbilical	uterus	amniotic	placenta

After fertilisation the .... implants in the lining of the uterus. The

.... fits closely into the wall of the .... It transfers

.... and food from the mother to the baby, and wastes such as

.... and carbon dioxide from the baby to the mother through the

.... cord. The .... fluid acts as a shock absorber and

helps to provide a stable environment for the growing foetus.

SECTION FIVE — GENETICS AND EVOLUTION

Questions on Inheritance and Genetic Diseases

Q1 a) Put a tick ✓ in the box ☐ next to each correct sentence about inheritance of sex (gender):

    ☐   Males have one X chromosome and one Y chromosome.

    ☐   Females have two X chromosomes.

    ☐   A sperm can contain an X chromosome or a Y chromosome.

    ☐   An egg can contain only a Y chromosome.

  b)   The sentence without a tick is incorrect.
Write down a correct version of it in the space below.

....

Q2   *The diagram below shows some of the events leading to the production of a baby.*

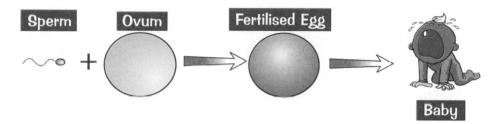

What is the fusing (joining) of the sperm and ovum called? ....

Q3   *When the sex chromosomes pair up at fertilisation, we get one chromosome from our father, and one from our mother. Depending on which chromosomes we get, we become male or female.*

The diagram on the right is a genetic diagram for the inheritance of a gene. This gene is in two forms, A and a. Study the diagram, then use it to help you answer the questions below.

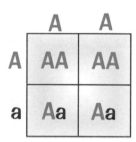

The empty genetic diagram below is to do with the inheritance of sex.

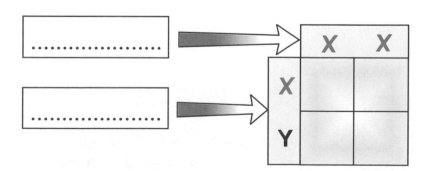

  a)   Label the arrows to show which chromosomes have come from the *father*, and which have come from the *mother*.

  b)   Complete the genetic diagram to show the *four* possible combinations of sex chromosomes.

  c)   In your completed genetic diagram, circle the combinations that would produce a *baby boy*.

  d)   How many combinations produce a *baby girl?* ....

SECTION FIVE — GENETICS AND EVOLUTION

Questions on Inheritance and Genetic Diseases

Q4 a) Fill in the boxes to complete the genetic diagram below showing the inheritance of sex:

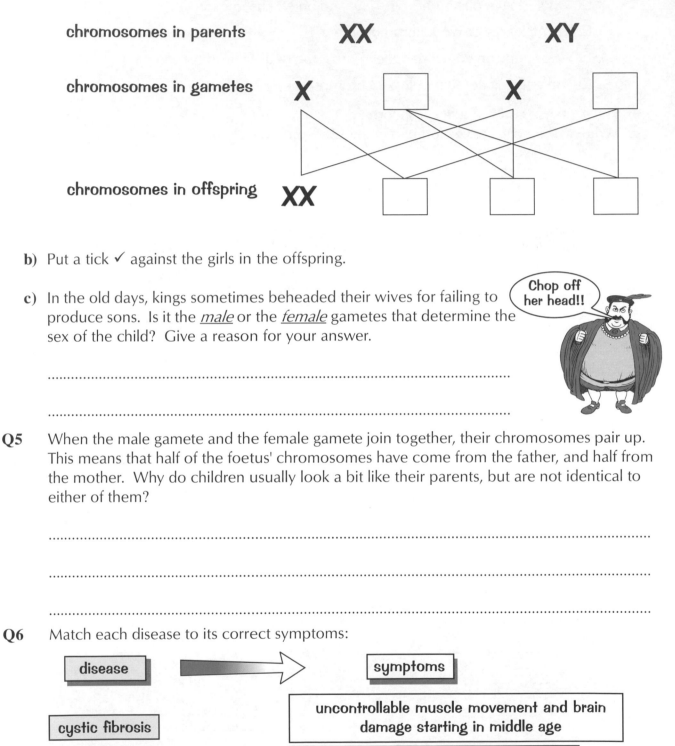

chromosomes in parents   **XX**   **XY**

chromosomes in gametes   **X**   **X**

chromosomes in offspring   **XX**

b) Put a tick ✓ against the girls in the offspring.

c) In the old days, kings sometimes beheaded their wives for failing to produce sons. Is it the *male* or the *female* gametes that determine the sex of the child? Give a reason for your answer.

Chop off her head!!

....

....

Q5 When the male gamete and the female gamete join together, their chromosomes pair up. This means that half of the foetus' chromosomes have come from the father, and half from the mother. Why do children usually look a bit like their parents, but are not identical to either of them?

....

....

....

Q6 Match each disease to its correct symptoms:

disease   ➡   symptoms

cystic fibrosis

haemophilia

Huntington's chorea

muscular dystrophy

sickle cell anaemia

uncontrollable muscle movement and brain damage starting in middle age

lots of thick mucus produced which causes breathing problems

progressive weakening of muscles starting in childhood

difficulty getting enough oxygen to the cells, painful swellings and skin ulcers

the blood does not clot properly

SECTION FIVE — GENETICS AND EVOLUTION

Questions on Inheritance and Genetic Diseases

Q7 *Sickle cell anaemia is a disorder of the red blood cells. It must be inherited from both parents. The parents need not have the disease. They can still pass it on without having it themselves if they are both carriers of the disease.*

a) What is a carrier? ....

b) Why can being a carrier of the disorder be an _advantage_ in countries where malaria is prevalent?

....

Q8 a) Complete the following paragraph about Cystic fibrosis

chest	mucus	genetic	defective	digestive	both

Cystic fibrosis is a .... disease. One in twenty people in this country

carry the .... gene. A person will only develop cystic fibrosis if they

inherit the gene from .... of their parents. Parents are often carriers of

the disorder without developing cystic fibrosis themselves. Sufferers' membranes

produce thick sticky .... in the lungs and pancreas causing

.... infections and .... problems.

b) How could you inherit the disease from parents who do not have the disease themselves?

....

Q9 a) Complete the following paragraph about Huntington's Chorea

mental	disease	worse	nervous	one

Huntington's Chorea is a disorder of the .... system. It can be inherited

from just .... parent who has the disorder. Symptoms only develop when the

person who has inherited the disorder is over 35-40 years of age. The ....

causes involuntary movements and .... deterioration. There is no cure

and the condition gets progressively ....

b) How is it possible that a young person has Huntington's Chorea without realising it?

....

SECTION FIVE — GENETICS AND EVOLUTION

Questions on Selective Breeding

Q1 *People in the Middle East were the first to use wheat to make bread. This is because wheat grew as a wild plant in the area (see map).*

a) From the pictures, name one feature for which the wheat has been selected.

....

b) *Over thousands of years, people developed the practice of eating the smaller seeds, and keeping the larger seeds to sow next year's crop.*
What feature were they selecting for?

....

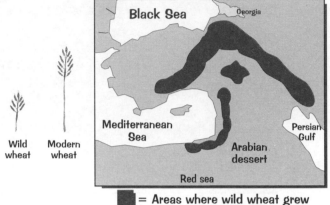

= Areas where wild wheat grew

Q2 *Lots of varieties of plant have been produced from a single type of plant, the brassica ancestor. Study the pictures on the right, then answer the question below.*

a) Selecting for large buds on the stem produced Brussels sprouts. Complete the table to show the features that plant breeders have selected when producing the other varieties.
One variety has been filled in for you already.

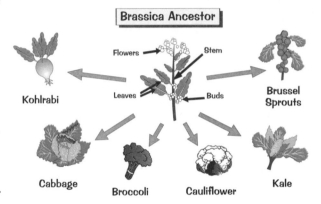

Feature selected		
leaf	flower	stem
	broccoli	

The flow diagram on the right outlines how kohlrabi was developed. Study it, then answer the questions.

Seeds only collected from brassica plants with thick stems → Grow plants from these seeds

b) What do you think the plant breeders did with the seeds from plants with thin stems?

....

c) How did they make sure that each generation of plant was more likely to have thick stems?

....

Q3 *Plant breeders often select for features that we cannot see, such as resistance to disease.*
Write down two other features that plant breeders might select for in crop plants.

1 .... 2 ....

Questions on Selective Breeding

Q4 *The Large White is a variety of pig often kept by farmers.*
It has been produced by selective breeding from wild boars.

Wild Boar

a) From the pictures, give two features that pig breeders
have selected for when producing the Large White.

Feature 1 ....

Feature 2 ....

Large White Pig

b) Give two features, not seen in pictures, that pig breeders might want to introduce.

1 .... 2 ....

Q5 *People have produced new varieties of dogs to achieve a particular look or temperament.*
All dogs have been bred from wolf ancestors.

Shar-pei   **Basset hound**   **Bedlington**   **Bulldog**

a) Give one feature of wolves that would not be found in varieties of pet dogs.

....

b) Give one feature of wolves that might be found in varieties of guard dogs.

....

c) Write down one feature that dog breeders have selected for when breeding Basset hounds.

....

d) Write down one feature of Basset hounds that you think would cause it problems, and why.

....

Q6 Complete the sentences below about selective breeding using the words from the list:

disease	varieties	animals	flavour	artificial	several	increased	sexual

Selective breeding is also called .... selection and involves ....

reproduction. We use it to produce new .... of animals and plants. It has

been used to produce crop plants and agricultural .... with

.... yield, improved .... and resistance to ....

Selective breeding can take .... generations.

SECTION FIVE — GENETICS AND EVOLUTION

Questions on Mutations

Q1 *Genes can change into new forms. These new forms of genes are called mutations.*

a) What is a *mutation?* ....

b) Put a tick ✓ in the box ☐ next to each correct sentence about mutations:

☐ Infra-red light can increase the chance of mutations occurring.

☐ X-rays can increase the chance of mutations occurring.

☐ Gamma radiation from radioactive substances can increase the chance of mutations.

☐ Chemicals called mutagens can increase the chance of mutations occurring.

c) The sentence without a tick is incorrect.
Write down a correct version of it in the space below.

....

Q2 *X-rays are used regularly in hospitals. X-rays can be blocked by lead.*

a) Give one reason why hospitals give people X-rays.

....

b) Why might you have to wear a lead-lined apron or patch when you have an X-ray?

....

c) Why do hospitals keep records of how many X-rays you have had?

....

d) Why are hospitals reluctant to X-ray pregnant women?

....

Q3 *Mutations can be a chemical change in just one gene, or they can be a major change in one or more chromosomes. The diagram on the right shows part of two fruit flies, and the chromosomes in a cell from each.*

a) What is the difference between the chromosomes in *cell A* and the chromosomes in *cell B?*

....

b) Circle the correct word in the brackets to complete these sentences:

The mis-shapen eye mutation might have been caused by (**a chemical / an accident**).

The mutation will be (**caught / inherited**) by the fly's offspring.

Q4 *Cancer can be caused by mutations that cause cells to grow uncontrollably.*

a) Cigarette smoke contains mutagens. What sort of cancer might they cause? ....

b) What sort of cancer might too much sunbathing cause? ....

c) What sort of cancer might chewing tobacco cause? ....

SECTION FIVE — GENETICS AND EVOLUTION

Questions on Mutations

Q5 *In parts of the country where homes have been built above granite rock the number of cancer cases is higher than average. This is because granite slowly releases radioactive radon gas, which collects in the houses. Radon gas does not smell and it is colourless.*

a) Circle the correct word in the brackets to complete the sentences below:

Radon causes mutations because it is (**colourless / radioactive**).

The more radon you are exposed to, the (**less / more**) mutations are likely to happen.

b) Suggest why houses built in these granite areas often have air extraction fans inside them.

....

c) What part of the body is radon most likely to affect? Give a reason for your answer.

....

Q6 *Down's Syndrome is a genetic disease caused by a fault in the way the chromosomes separate when the mother's gametes are being formed. People with Down's Syndrome can live very fulfilled lives, but suffer from learning difficulties and a shortened life-span.*
Study the diagram on the right, then answer these questions:

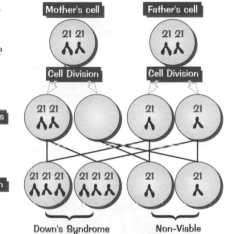

a) Which chromosome is involved? ....

b) If the child receives only one of these chromosomes, is it able to survive to birth? ....

c) Study the table on the right. What happens to the chance of a woman having a Down's Syndrome child as she gets older?

Mother's age	Chance of having a child with Down's Syndrome
25	1 in 1400
40	1 in 110
45	1 in 30

....

Q7 *A sheep with very short legs appeared in a farmer's flock in the 18th century. The farmer bred from the sheep and eventually produced a variety of sheep called Ancorn sheep.*

a) Why might a sheep with short legs appear in a normal flock?

....

b) Why would some of the offspring from the sheep also have short legs?

....

c) Suggest an advantage to the farmer of keeping short-legged Ancorn sheep.

....

d) *Most mutations are not an advantage to the animal or plant involved.*
Is having short legs an advantage to the Ancorn sheep? Explain your answer.

....

....

SECTION FIVE — GENETICS AND EVOLUTION

Questions on Fossils and Evolution

Q1   *Fossils are the remains of animals and plants that died many years ago.*
Normally when organisms die, they decay.
If the conditions needed for decay are not there, they may be fossilised.

Olenellus
(trilobite)

The pictures below show three types of fossils. Peat Bog Man was preserved
because there was little oxygen in the water-logged peat, and the acidic
conditions made it difficult for decay bacteria to grow.

Draw lines to match the insect and the mammoth to the missing conditions for decay.

Peat Bog Man.
Body found in
water-logged
acidic peat.

Insect.
Found in
amber formed
when tree gum
turns solid.

Mammoth.
Found in
an icy
glacier.

| oxygen missing | warmth missing | moisture missing |

Q2   *In some cases, fossils form from hard parts that do not decay easily. The diagrams below*
show the processes involved in fossilising an animal with a shell, but they are in the wrong
order.

a)   Write numbers in the boxes to get the correct order, starting with 1 and ending with 4.
Number 3 has been done for you.

b)   In number 3, the calcite in the shell is being replaced with minerals. This takes a long time.
Why are the soft body parts of the animal not replaced by minerals in the same way?

....

Q3   Complete the sentences below about fossils using the words from this list:

decay	conditions	rocks	animals	minerals	oxygen	hard

Fossils are the remains of plants or .... from many years ago which are found

in .... Many fossils are formed from .... parts which do not

.... easily. These parts are eventually replaced by .... Some fossils

form because one or more of the .... needed for decay are missing. For decay

to happen, ..., moisture, warmth and non-acidic conditions are needed.

Questions on Fossils and Evolution

Q4 *Species can become extinct if the environment they need to survive changes, or if new predators, diseases or competitors are introduced.*

a) Dinosaurs are extinct today. How do we know that they once existed at all?

....

b) Why don't we know for sure how the dinosaurs became extinct?

....

c) Write down two things that might have happened to cause the dinosaurs to become extinct.

1 .... 2 ....

Q5 *Life on Earth is thought to be very old, with the first simple living things developing more than three billion years ago. The theory of evolution says that all the species of organisms alive today, and others that are now extinct, evolved from other simpler organisms.*

The horse evolved to its modern appearance over millions of years. Study the diagram on the right, then answer the questions below.

a) How tall was the oldest ancestor of the horse?

Height .... m

b) How do we know what the feet and teeth of these ancestors looked like?

....

Evolution of the horse

| Time scale | 55 million years ago | | 25 million years ago | | 2 million years ago |

Type of Horse

Hyracotherium (0.4m), Mesohippus (0.6m), Merychippus (1.0m), Pliohippus (1.0m), Modern (1.6m)

Type of Teeth — Top surface, Bottom surface

Type of Forefeet

c) The earliest teeth were flat with no ridges to cope with soft food. How have the teeth evolved to cope with tough grasses? ....

d) Modern horses are adapted to run quickly and to see into the distance. From the evidence in the diagrams, how have horses evolved to do these things?

....

e) What would have happened if the ancestors of the horse had been *unable* to evolve?

....

f) What causes a feature in living things to change so that this change is passed to their offspring?

....

Questions on Population Sizes

Q1 *There are twelve sycamore trees in a wood. Their environment is quite sunny, with plenty of nutrients in the soil. They share the wood with many other plants and animals.*

a) What is the environment of the sycamore trees?

....

b) What is the population of sycamore trees?

....

c) What is the habitat of the sycamore trees?

....

d) What is the community in the wood?

....

e) Match up the statements below to make a correct *sentence.* The first one is done for you.

population means	→	the conditions in which an organism lives
community means		a place with particular conditions where certain organisms live
habitat means		a group of different living organisms sharing a place in which to live
environment means	→	the number of individuals of a particular species

Q2 *In an experiment, a species of bacterium was grown in a Petri dish. The Petri dish had a layer of jelly-like agar for the bacteria to grow on, and there were nutrients in the agar to feed the bacteria.*

The Petri dish was checked regularly for a few days. The number of bacteria was estimated each time by measuring the size of the bacterial colony.

The graph on the right shows the results obtained.

colony of bacteria

Petri dish with agar

a) Circle the correct word in each of the following underlined pairs:

number of bacteria

time

The Petri dish is the habitat / environment of the bacteria.

The number of bacteria in the dish is the community / population.

b) *Near the end of the experiment, the number of bacteria reaches a maximum.* Give *two* reasons why the number of bacteria does not just keep on going up.

Reason 1 ....

Reason 2 ....

c) *Some of the bacteria are scraped off, and put onto some fresh agar in another Petri dish. They begin to increase in number just as they did in the first experiment. Why?*

....

Questions on Population Sizes

Q3 *The chart on the right shows the change in the numbers of a species of predator and its prey.*

Prey   Predator

Number of animals

Time

a) Explain what the word predator means.

....

....

b) Explain what the word prey means.

....

c) Give one example of a predator and its prey.

Predator ....   Its prey ....

d) Put a tick in the box next to each correct sentence about the graph above:

The number of predators decreases because the number of prey increases.	☐
The number of predators decreases because the number of prey decreases.	☐
If the population of prey increases, more food is available for its predators.	☐
The population is not usually limited by the amount of food available.	☐

e) Look at your answers to part d). The sentences without a tick are incorrect. Write a correct version of each incorrect sentence below.

....

....

Q4 *The number of mice in a wood was estimated at the same time each year for thirteen years.*

The results are shown in the bar chart on the right.

Number of mice

Number of mice

1 2 3 4 5 6 7 8 9 10 11 12 13
Year of Study

a) Give two possible reasons why the number of mice in the wood fell between years 4 and 5.

....

....

b) Give two possible reasons why the number of mice increased between years 6 and 7, but don't write the opposite of your answers to part a).

....

....

SECTION SIX — THE ENVIRONMENT

116

Questions on Communities (Adapt and Survive)

Q1 *The graph below shows the average daytime temperature (line) and rainfall (bars) on the northern edge of the Sahara desert.*

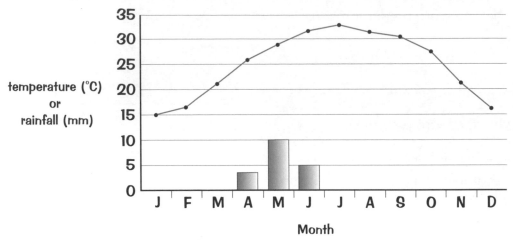

a) What is the environment like in the desert?

....

b) What will happen to animals and plants if they are not adapted to the desert?

....

Q2 *Desert plants have adaptations that let them survive the desert environment.*
Match the statements about the way plants have adapted.

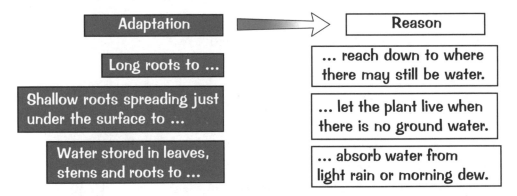

Q3 a) Put a tick in the box next to each correct sentence about desert plants:

Some plants drop their leaves during a dry spell. [ ]

They usually have large leaves. [ ]

Their stomata (pores in the leaves) are closed during the day. [ ]

b) The sentence without a tick is incorrect. Write a correct version of it in the space below.

....

c) Why do desert plants have these adaptations? ....

d) Why do many desert plants have thorns? ....

Questions on Communities (Adapt and Survive)

Q4   *The sidewinder adder lives in deserts. It moves sideways across the sand by throwing its body into a series of S-shapes, always keeping a loop off the ground, with two other parts touching.*
Why does it do this?

....

....

Q5   *Many desert animals, such as the kangaroo rat, spend the day in a burrow and come out only at night.*

a) Write down two advantages of doing this.

Advantage 1 ....

Advantage 2 ....

b) Write down a disadvantage of doing this.

....

Q6   *Camels are probably the best-known animals in the desert. There are two types, the Bactrian camel (right) and the Arabian camel or dromedary (left).*

a) Describe the features that the camels have in common which make them adapted for desert conditions.

....

....

b) *The Bactrian camel is found in high rocky deserts where it gets very cold in winter.*
From the picture, what adaptation does the Bactrian camel have to allow it to survive there?

....

c) *It has been discovered that a shaved camel loses nearly twice as much body water as an unshaved camel. Suggest why losing its hair could cause this difference.*

....

d) *Humans need to maintain a fairly constant body temperature, but camels can tolerate a big change in their body temperature.*
Camels can allow the temperature to go from about 34°C to 41°C during the day, and then they cool off during the night. This means that during the day they do not need to use the methods of cooling that humans do.
How is this advantageous to the camel?

....

....

Questions on Communities (Adapt and Survive)

Q7 *The graph below shows the average daytime temperature (line) and rainfall (bars) in the Arctic.*

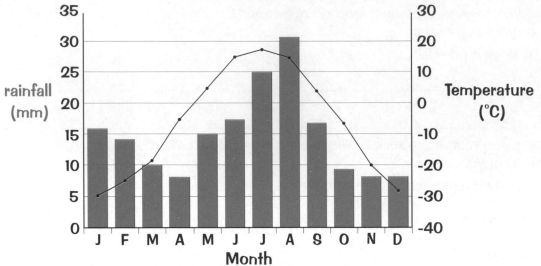

a) What is the temperature range throughout the year in the arctic?

....

b) What is the environment like in the summer months of May to September?

....

....

c) What is the environment like during the rest of the year?

....

....

Q8 *It's not all sea-ice in the Arctic. There is a lot of windswept land in the Arctic called the Tundra. The plants there often grow very close to the ground.*

a) Why do the plants grow like this?

....

....

b) The plants also have small leaves. Suggest one possible reason for this.

Reason ....

c) In the Summer, it is warm enough for mosquitoes. What problem will they cause the animals in the tundra?

....

Questions on Communities (Adapt and Survive)

Q9 *Large animals have a small surface area to volume ratio.
This means that they lose heat more slowly than animals
with a large surface area to volume ratio.*

a) Why do polar bears and walruses have
large bodies with lots of fat?

....

....

....

b) Lemmings are small rodents that live in the tundra, and have a rounded body about 12cm
long. Why do lemmings live in burrows?

....

....

....

Q10 *Animals have adapted in many ways to allow them to survive in their surroundings.*

a) Why does the snowshoe hare have white fur in the winter and red-brown fur in the
summer?

....

....

b) Desert foxes have very large ears, but Arctic foxes only have very small ears.
Suggest a reason for this difference (it is not to do with hearing or hiding).

....

....

c) Indian elephants have smaller ears than African elephants. Explain why this adaptation is
important to the elephants living in these countries.

....

....

Q11 Complete the sentences below using the words from this list:

plants	fat	environments	camouflage	body	insulation	adapted

Animals are .... to different .... They can have different

.... sizes, different amounts of .... and fur for ....

They might also use .... also show adaptations.

Questions on Atmospheric Pollution

Q1 *The pie chart below shows the amounts of the main gases in the atmosphere.*

  a) Match the various gases to the correct percentage present in the atmosphere:

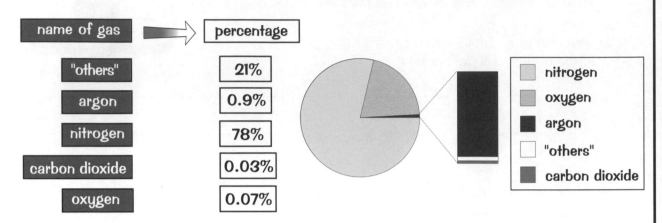

| name of gas | → | percentage |

"others"	21%
argon	0.9%
nitrogen	78%
carbon dioxide	0.03%
oxygen	0.07%

Legend:
- nitrogen
- oxygen
- argon
- "others"
- carbon dioxide

  b) *Atmospheric pollution involves adding more carbon dioxide and more gases to the "others".* What do you notice about the amounts of these gases in the atmosphere?

  ....

Q2 *When coal, oil or natural gas burn, the carbon in them reacts with oxygen to form carbon dioxide.*

  a) What type of fuel are coal, oil and natural gas? ....

  b) Circle the correct word in the <u>underlined</u> pair:

  When oil is burnt, the amount of carbon dioxide in the atmosphere goes <u>up</u> / <u>down</u>.

Q3 *If fuels do not burn completely, particles of black carbon are made. This is called soot.* Suggest a problem that plants will have if soot settles on their leaves.

  ....

Q4 a) *Many fuels contain small amounts of sulphur.* Name the gas made when sulphur burns in air.
  Name of gas ....

  b) *The line on the chart show the amount of this gas near a factory.*
  The bars shows the number of people with bronchitis in the surrounding area.

  What conclusion can you make about this gas and bronchitis?

  Amount of Gas

  Number of people with bronchitis

  Distance from factory (km)

  ....

  ....

Questions on Atmospheric Pollution

Q5 *Ozone is made when electric sparks or lightning pass through oxygen. Ozone is a gas with a strong smell. It can often be smelt near electrical equipment such as photocopiers and laser printers, or in the air after thunderstorms. Ozone can cause breathing problems and stinging eyes.*

  a) Why is ozone a health hazard? ....

  b) Why should photocopiers and laser printers only be used in well-ventilated rooms?

  ....

Q6 *Ozone created at ground level is dangerous, but 25-50 km above us ozone reaches its maximum natural concentration. This is the ozone layer, which absorbs ultraviolet light from the Sun.* Suggest two things that would happen to plants and animals if the ozone layer were destroyed.

  1) ....

  2) ....

Q7 Chlorofluorocarbons (CFC's) have many uses. Match the *properties* to the correct *uses*:

properties	→	uses
non-toxic		polystyrene food containers
low boiling		aerosol sprays
very unreactive		fire extinguishers

Q8 *CFC's cause ozone in the ozone layer to break down. The Montreal Protocol is an international agreement to stop making most CFC's and to use "ozone friendly" gases instead. This is already happening, but the ozone layer will continue to be damaged for many years.* Why is this the case?

  ....

  ....

Q9 *The Sun gives us heat and light. It also produces ultraviolet light (UV light) which we cannot see.*

  a) Ultraviolet light can damage proteins. Why do people who work outside in the Mediterranean often have darkened skin and lots of wrinkles?

  ....

  ....

  b) Ozone can break down chlorophyll in plants. What problems would this cause to plants?

  ....

  c) Ultraviolet light can also damage the chromosomes in the cell nucleus. What could happen to pale-skinned people who sunbathe too much?

  ....

Questions on The Greenhouse Effect

Q1 a) *The temperature on the surface of the Moon ranges from -175°C to 125°C.*
The average temperature on the surface of the Moon is about -20°C.

If the Moon had air, would we be able to survive there? Explain your answer.

....

....

b) *The Earth and the Moon are both the same average distance from the Sun and both get their heat from the Sun.*
From this information, predict what the temperature of the Earth's surface should be.

Range of temperature: ....°C to ....°C   Average temperature: ....°C

c) *The temperature on the surface of the Earth actually ranges from -89°C to 58°C, with an average of 14°C.* Give two differences between your predicted temperatures in part (b) with the actual temperatures on the surface of the Earth.

Difference 1: ....

Difference 2: ....

Q2 *The differences between the Moon's surface temperature and the Earth's surface temperature are because the Earth has an atmosphere.*
Our atmosphere traps heat by a process known as the <u>greenhouse effect</u>.

Complete the diagram on the right to show how the greenhouse effect works.

Choose from these labels:

Earth's surface
Earth's atmosphere
Heat from the Sun
Heat absorbed by the atmosphere

Q3 Complete the paragraph about the greenhouse effect using the correct words from the list:

good	absorbed	surface	Sun	atmosphere	space	warms

Energy from the .... passes through the Earth's .... and

warms the Earth's surface. Heat energy from the Earth's .... is radiated

into .... but some of it is .... by gases in the atmosphere.

This .... the atmosphere, which is .... for life on Earth.

123

Questions on The Greenhouse Effect

Q4 *Look at the graphs below. They show the amount of carbon released from burning fossil fuels each year since 1850, and the percentage of carbon dioxide in the air each year since 1850.*

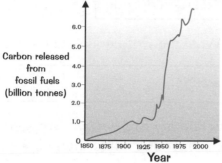 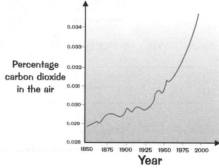

a) How has the amount of carbon released changed in the hundred years from 1850 to 1950?

....

b) How has the amount of carbon released changed since 1950?

....

c) How has the percentage of carbon dioxide in the air changed between 1850 and 1950?

....

d) How has the percentage of carbon dioxide in the air changed since 1950?

....

e) Where do you think a lot of the carbon dioxide has come from? Explain your answer.

....

Q5 *The graphs below show the changes in average temperatures and sea level since 1880.*

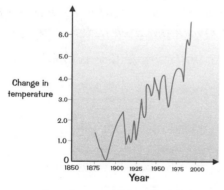 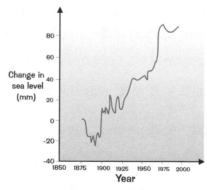

Suggest why the sea level has changed in this way. Explain your answer.

....

....

Q6 Using your answers to Questions 4 and 5, suggest why the average temperatures have changed.

....

Q7 Suggest two problems that the greenhouse effect and global warming might cause.

Problem 1 ....

Problem 2 ....

SECTION SIX — THE ENVIRONMENT

124

Questions on Acid Rain

Q1 *Carbon reacts with oxygen to make carbon dioxide. The word equation for this reaction is shown in the box.*

carbon + oxygen ⟹ carbon dioxide

Hydrogen reacts with oxygen to make water. Write the word equation for this reaction in the box.

⟹

Q2 *Petrol is made of hydrocarbons. Hydrocarbons contain carbon and hydrogen atoms only.* Use your answer to question 1 to complete the word equation for burning petrol in the box below:

petrol + oxygen ⟹ .... + ...

Q3 *Many fuels contain sulphur.* Underline the gas made when sulphur burns in oxygen:

nitrogen oxides   carbon dioxide   sulphur dioxide   water

Q4 *Car engines can get so hot, that nitrogen in the air reacts with oxygen to produce nitrogen oxides.*
Look at your answers to questions 2 and 3. Write down the names of four substances that will be made when petrol burns in a car engine.

1) ....   3) ....

2) ....   4) ....

Q5 *Katie tested some rainwater samples with universal indicator solution to find out how acidic they were. She matched the colours on a chart to work out their pH numbers.*

Rainwater sample A was pH 6, sample B was pH 2, and sample C was pH 4.

a) Which sample, A, B or C was the most acidic? Sample ....

b) Which sample, A, B or C was probably uncontaminated rain? Sample ....

Q6 *When carbon dioxide dissolves in water, carbonic acid is made. Air is about 0.035% carbon dioxide.* Why is rainwater naturally acidic?

....

....

Q7 Match the various gases to the correct acids that they make:

| Name of Gas | ⟹ | Acid Solution |

nitrogen oxides makes ...   carbonic acid

sulphur dioxide makes ...   nitric acid

carbon dioxide makes ...   sulphuric acid

SECTION SIX — THE ENVIRONMENT

Questions on Acid Rain

Q8   *The table on the left shows the amount of acid rain gases from different sources.*

The percentage contributions of nitrogen oxides have been plotted on the graph below.

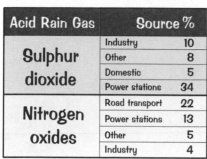

Acid Rain Gas	Source %	
Sulphur dioxide	Industry	10
	Other	8
	Domestic	5
	Power stations	34
Nitrogen oxides	Road transport	22
	Power stations	13
	Other	5
	Industry	4

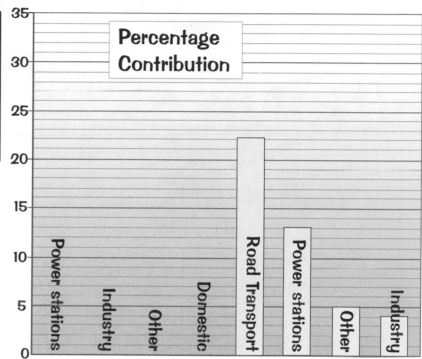

Source of acid rain gases

a) Complete the graph to show the percentage contributions of sulphur dioxide from the different sources.

b) Which source produces the most sulphur dioxide?

   Name of source ....

c) Which source produces the most nitrogen oxides?

   Name of source ....

d) Which source produces the most acid rain gases?

   Name of source ....

Q9 a) What gases dissolve in clouds to make acid rain?

   Names of gases: ....

b) What acids can be found in acid rain?

   Names of acids: ....

Questions on Farming and its Problems

Q1 *Three hundred years ago, there were about 600 million people in the world. There are about ten times that number now. Farming methods have changed a lot so that everyone can be fed.*
The maps below show a farming area about one hundred years ago, and present day.

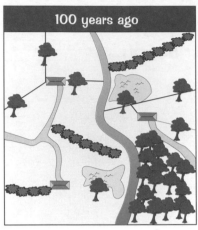

Key to Maps

🌳 Tree
Pond
🌲 Hedge
▬ Stream
✉ Bulding
＼ Fence
▭ Road

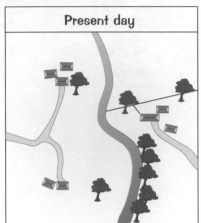

100 years ago

Present day

a) What changes can you see in the size of the fields? ....

b) Write down four things that have been done to change the size of the fields in this way.

1 .... 2 ....

3 .... 4 ....

Q2 a) Put a tick in the box next to each correct sentence about *modern farming methods*:

Farms are much smaller than they used to be, and have more fields.	☐
Fields are much bigger than they used to be.	☐
Combine harvesters and tractors make it easier to farm large fields.	☐
Farms have more hedgerows and trees than they used to.	☐
Wild animals and plants have fewer habitats in which to live.	☐

b) The sentences without a tick are incorrect. Write down the correct version of the sentences in the spaces below.

....

....

Q3 *Complete the sentences below using the words from this list:*

erosion	loss	increased	habitat	larger	more

Fields have .... in size to help produce .... food.

These .... fields have caused a .... of

.... for wildlife, and more soil ....

Questions on Farming and its Problems

Q4   *This question is about pesticides. Match the pesticide with the correct function.*

| Pesticide | $\Rightarrow$ | Function |

herbicide	kills insects that eat crops
insecticide	kills fungi that cause disease in plants
fungicide	kills weeds that compete with crops

Q5   Look at this food chain, then answer the questions:

rose bush $\Longrightarrow$ greenfly $\Longrightarrow$ ladybird $\Longrightarrow$ great tit

a)   Circle the correct answer from each of the <u>underlined</u> pairs:

Insecticide will kill the <u>rose bush</u> / <u>greenfly</u>.

Ladybirds eat <u>great tits</u> / <u>greenfly</u>.

If there are fewer greenfly, there will be <u>more</u> / <u>less</u> food for the great tits.

b)   Look at your answers to part a). Explain briefly what might happen to great tits if a gardener uses an insecticide spray to protect their rose bushes.

....

....

Q6 a) Put a tick in the box next to each correct sentence about *insecticides*:

Insecticides kill insects.	☐
If insecticides kill bees, more flowers will be pollinated.	☐
The use of insecticides provides more food for many birds.	☐

b)   Look at the sentences without a tick. Write down the correct version of the sentence.

....

....

Q7   *Complete the sentences below using the words from the list:*

| fish   fertilisers   insects   minerals   pollinating   chains   pesticides   oxygen |

Farmers use .... to kill .... and other

pests that reduce crop yields. The use of these chemicals can disturb food

.... and reduce the number of .... insects.

Farmers use .... to replace lost .... in the

soil, but they can cause the amount of .... in rivers to

decrease, and so reduce the number of .... and other animals.

SECTION SIX — THE ENVIRONMENT

Questions on Foodwebs

Q1 a) What do we call organisms that can make their own food? ....

b) What do we call organisms that rely on other organisms for their food? ....

Q2 Match the statements below to form correct sentences:

Carnivores are		animals that eat other animals.
Herbivores are		animals that can eat both plants and other animals.
Omnivores are		animals that eat plants.

Q3 *Look at this food chain:* grass → rabbit → fox.

Fill in the table below with the correct organisms. One of the consumers has been filled in for you.

description	producer	consumer	consumer	herbivore	carnivore
organism			fox		

Q4 Producers make food by photosynthesis.
What type of living things are producers? ....

Q5 *Study this woodland food web. It shows all the woodland food chains interconnected.*

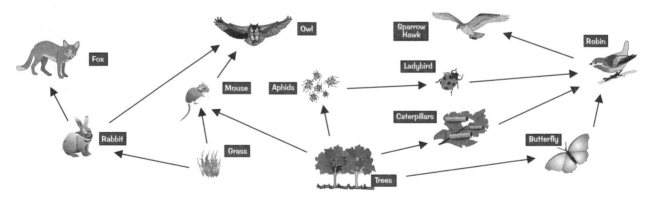

a) Name one producer in this food web. ....

b) Name one secondary consumer in this food web. ....

c) Write down the longest food chain in this food web:

....

d) Which animal eats the greatest range of foods? ....

e) Name one animal that is not eaten by anything. ....

f) What general name is given to animals that are not eaten by anything? ....

SECTION SIX — THE ENVIRONMENT

Questions on Foodwebs

Q6 a) Make a food chain in the space below using these organisms:

blue tit   caterpillar   hawk   oak tree

.... $\rightarrow$ .... $\rightarrow$ .... $\rightarrow$ ....

b) Match the animal to its position in the food chain.

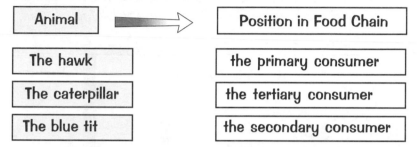

Animal	Position in Food Chain
The hawk	the primary consumer
The caterpillar	the tertiary consumer
The blue tit	the secondary consumer

Q7 *Look at the food web below, then answer these questions.*

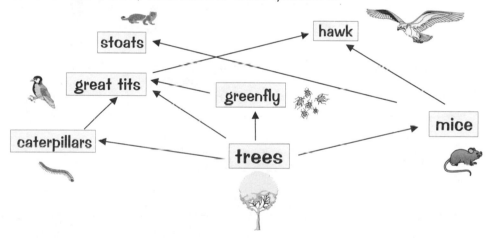

a) Which of the animals is an omnivore? ....

b) Why is the animal in part a) an omnivore? ....

c) Complete these sentences about the numbers of animals in the food web.
Circle the correct word from each of the <u>underlined</u> pairs.

If the hawk dies, the number of great tits will <u>go up</u> / <u>go down</u>.

If the stoats die, the number of mice will <u>go up</u> / <u>go down</u>.

If the numbers of caterpillars and greenfly go down, the number of great tits will <u>go up</u> / <u>go down</u>.

If the numbers of mice increase the hawk will have <u>more</u> / <u>less</u> food.

d) *Some mink escape from a farm and start eating the mice.*

Will the number of mice go up, down, or stay the same? ....

Questions on Foodwebs

Q8 *Dead animals and plants are also a source of food in communities.*

a) What name is given to organisms that break down dead animals and plant material?

....

b) Give two examples of organisms that break down dead animals and plant material.

....

Q9 *The food web below shows some of the organisms found on the Grand Banks off the coast of Newfoundland. The Grand Banks have been an important fishing ground.*

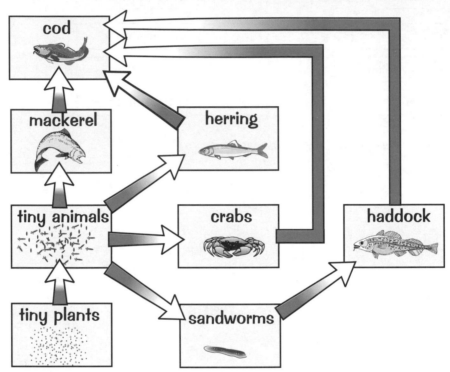

a) What would happen to the number of haddock if the number of sandworms went up?

....

....

b) What would happen to the number of cod if the number of tiny animals went down?

....

....

c) *People have caught too many mackerel and herring, causing their numbers to go down. Some trawlers have also damaged the sea bed, killing the crabs and sandworms there.*

Explain the effects these changes will have on the numbers of haddock, cod and tiny animals on the Grand Banks.

....

....

....

Questions on Pyramids of Numbers and Biomass

Q1 *Look at this food chain:* carrot → rabbit → fox

a) What food does the rabbit eat? ....

b) In the food chain, there were 4000 carrots, 100 rabbits, and 1 fox.
Which pyramid of numbers below, A, B or C, is the correct one for this food chain?

Correct pyramid is ....

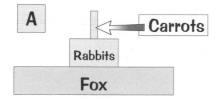

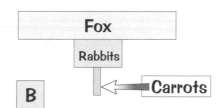

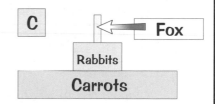

Q2 *The diagram below is a pyramid of numbers. The bar showing the tertiary consumers has been labelled for you. The other bars have not.*

Identify which bar corresponds to the other letters.

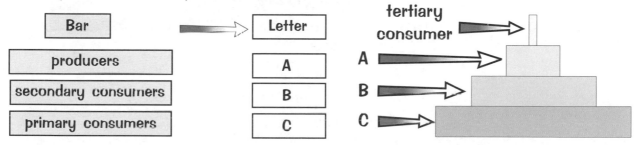

Bar	Letter
producers	A
secondary consumers	B
primary consumers	C

Q3 Draw pyramids of numbers for the following food chains. Use the space at the bottom of the page. When you draw your pyramids, make sure you do the following things:

Use a ruler and sharp pencil.

Label each step with the name and number of the living thing.

a) tiny plants (10,000) → water fleas (2,000) → trout (1)

b) rose bush (1) → greenfly (100) → ladybirds (20) → great tit (2)

Pyramid a)

Pyramid b)

Questions on Pyramids of Numbers and Biomass

Q4 *Read the following sentences about biomass and pyramids of biomass and put a tick in the boxes next to the correct sentences.*

Biomass is the number of living things.	☐
Biomass is the mass of living material.	☐
Pyramids of biomass show the biomass at each stage in a food chain.	☐
Pyramids of biomass cannot be drawn to scale.	☐
The biomass gets less going from the beginning to the end of a food chain.	☐

Q5 *One of the food chains in the North Sea is:*

tiny plants → tiny animals → mackerel → cod.

The biomass of each living thing is shown in the table.

organism	biomass in kg
cod	2
mackerel	10
tiny animals	80
tiny plants	100

Draw the pyramid of biomass for this food chain in the space below. We suggest you use a scale of 1mm for each kg.

Questions on Pyramids of Numbers and Biomass

Q6 *Look at the pyramid on the right.*

a) What sort of pyramid is shown on the right?
<u>Underline</u> the correct answer:

pyramid of numbers / pyramid of biomass

b) Write down a reason for your answer to part a).

....

....

Q7 Draw lines to match the descriptions to the correct pyramid. The pyramids can be used twice.

The pyramid of numbers for a community that starts with a large producer.	The pyramid of biomass for a woodland community.	The pyramid of numbers for an ocean community in which the producers are tiny plants.	The pyramid of numbers for a food chain that ends with tiny fleas.

Q8 Complete the sentences below using the words from this list:

pyramids	chain	food	biomass	narrower	numbers	living

Pyramids of .... show the number of organisms at each stage

of a .... chain. Pyramids of .... show the mass

of .... material at each stage of a food ....

Pyramids of biomass get .... near the top, but

.... of number can be any shape.

Questions on The Carbon Cycle

Q1 *There are two equations you need to know: one for photosynthesis and one for respiration.*

  a) Complete the word equation below for photosynthesis:

    Carbon dioxide + ... → glucose + ...

  b) Complete the word equation below for respiration:

    .... + oxygen → water + ...

Q2 The diagram on the right shows part of the carbon cycle. Use your answers to question 1 to fill in the missing words. Choose from the list below left (you will not need them all):

photosynthesis

respiration

oxygen

carbon dioxide

water

glucose

....
in the atmosphere

....

....

Carbon Compounds in plants

Q3 a) What gas, found in air, is needed for burning to happen? ....

  b) *Water vapour is produced when wood burns.*
    What other gas is produced when wood burns? ....

  c) Complete the word equation for wood burning. Use your answers to parts a) and b) to help you.

    wood + ... → .... + ...

Q4 Fill in the missing words in the sentences below. Choose from this list of words:

glucose up down respiration oxygen photosynthesis burn carbon dioxide

Plants make glucose from .... and water. This process is called

.... It causes the amount of carbon dioxide in the air to go

.... Animals, plants and bacteria produce energy from

.... using the process called ....

This process causes the amount of carbon dioxide in the air to go ....

When wood and other fuels ...., ... from the

air is used up, and more carbon dioxide is produced.

Questions on The Carbon Cycle

Q5 *Bacteria and fungi are decomposers. They can break down solid waste materials from animals. They can also break down materials in dead animals and plants. This breakdown is called decay.*

  a) What can decomposers do? ....

  ....

  b) What is decay? ....

  ....

  c) Name two types of living thing that can cause decay: .... and ....

Q6 Complete these sentences about decay by microbes. Circle the correct word from each of the <u>underlined</u> pairs:

  a) Microbes break down materials faster when they are <u>cool</u> / <u>warm</u>, and in <u>moist</u> / <u>dry</u> conditions.

  b) Many microbes work better if there is more <u>oxygen</u> / <u>nitrogen</u> in their environment.

Q7 Match the statements below to show the effect the three processes have on the amount of carbon dioxide in the air.

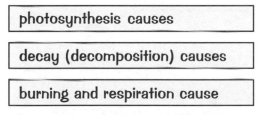

| photosynthesis causes |
| decay (decomposition) causes |
| burning and respiration cause |

| carbon dioxide in the air to increase |
| carbon dioxide in the air to decrease |

Q8 *Look at the diagram of the carbon cycle below.*
  Fill in the missing words to complete the diagram. Choose from the list below (some words may not be needed, and some words might be needed more than once):

  animals   plants   decay   burning   feeding   respiration   photosynthesis

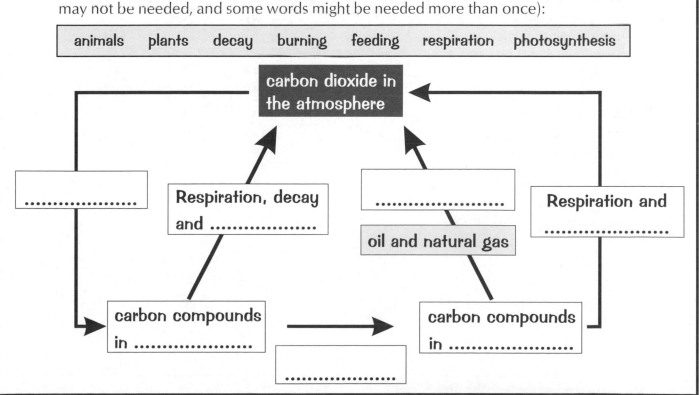

General Certificate of Secondary Education

Science: Double Award
(Co-ordinated and Modular)
Foundation Paper: Trial Examination

Monday 7 June 1999 9.30 am — 11.00 am
Monday 14 June 1999 9.30am — 11.00 am

Centre name								
Centre number					Candidate number			
Surname								
Other names								

(F)

In addition to this paper you will need
- Calculator
- Pencil
- Pen

Time
- 1 hour 30 minutes.

Instructions to candidates
- Write your name and other details in the spaces provided above.
- Answer **all** the questions in this paper.
- Write your answers in this combined question paper/answer book.
- Write your answers in blue or black ink or ballpoint pen.
- Do all rough work on the paper.

Information for candidates
- The number of marks is given in brackets at the end of each question or part-question.
- Marks will not be deducted for incorrect answers.
- You are reminded of the need for good English and clear presentation.
- In calculations show clearly how you work out your answers.

Paper One

For examiner's use	
Page 137	
138	
139	
140	
141	
142	
143	
144	
145	
146	
Total	

Paper Two

For examiner's use	
Page 147	
148	
149	
150	
151	
152	
153	
154	
Total	

1) The pictures show a toy teddy bear and a brown bear.

Write down **three** ways that we can tell that a brown bear is alive, but a teddy bear is not.

1 ....

2 ....

3 ....

(3 marks)

2) The diagram below shows a plant cell.

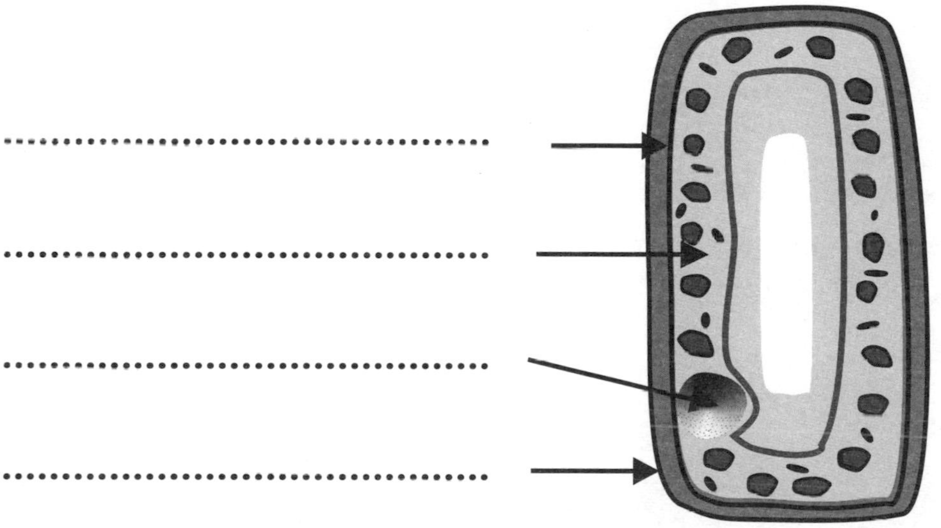

....

....

....

....

a) Use words from the list below to label the parts of the plant cell.

nucleus   **cell wall**   **cell membrane**   **cytoplasm**

(4 marks)

b) Use words from the list above to complete the sentences about cells.

The .... controls the movement of substances into and out of the cell.

Most of the chemical reactions in the cell happen in the ....

The .... controls the activities of the cell.

(3 marks)

c) Cell walls are not found in animal cells.

Write down the names of **two** other features, not labelled in the diagram, that are only found in plant cells.

1 ....

2 ....

(2 marks)

3) a) What do we call a group of cells with a similar structure that carry out a particular function?

....

(1 mark)

b) Write down an example of a group of cells like this.

....

(1 mark)

4) a) Why are carbohydrates and fats important in a healthy diet?

....

(1 marks)

b) Meat is a good source of protein. Name **one** other good source of protein in the diet.

Name of source ....

(1 mark)

c) Explain briefly why proteins are important in our diet.

....

....

(2 marks)

SECTION SEVEN — TRIAL EXAM

5) a) The drawing below shows part of the human digestive system.

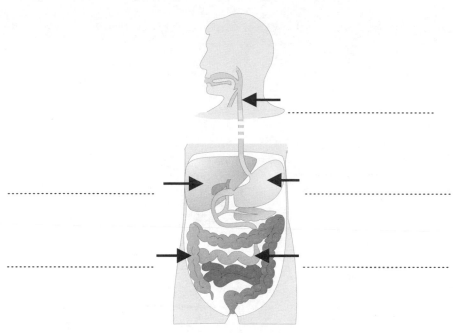

On the drawing, use guidelines to label the following:
i)   stomach

ii) liver

iii) small intestine

iv) large intestine

v)   oesophagus (gullet)

(5 marks)

b) What happens to food that cannot be digested?

....
(1 mark)

c) Where is water absorbed in the digestive system?

....
(1 mark)

d) Explain, as fully as you can, what happens to the **starch** when we eat a piece of bread.

....

....

....

....
(4 marks)

SECTION SEVEN — TRIAL EXAM

6) The diagram below shows the human breathing system.

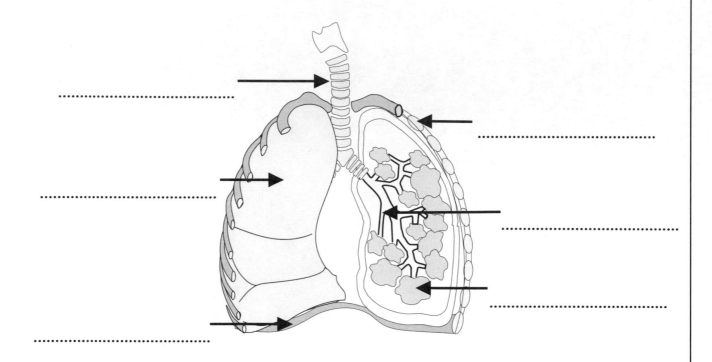

....

....

....

....

....

a) Use words from the list below to label the parts of the breathing system.

rib   **trachea**   **bronchiole**   **lung**   **diaphragm**   **alveoli**

(5 marks)

b) What name is given to the part of the body where the lungs are found?

Name of part ....

(1 mark)

c) The diagram below shows a section through an alveolus, with blood flowing through a blood vessel in close contact with it.

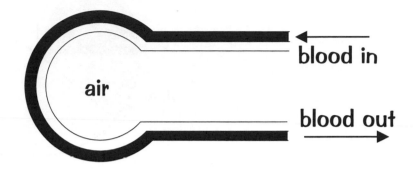

i) Will the blood going in have more, or less, oxygen in it than the blood going out?

....
(1 mark)

ii) Will the air going out have more, or less, carbon dioxide in it than the air going in?

....
(1 mark)

iii) Name the process that allows gases to be exchanged between the air and the blood.

....
(1 mark)

d) Tobacco smoke can damage the lungs.

i) Name a disease of the lungs that can be caused by tobacco smoke.

....
(1 mark)

ii) What is the addictive substance in tobacco smoke?

....
(1 mark)

SECTION SEVEN — TRIAL EXAM

7) The pie chart shows the proportions of acid rain
gases released in the UK recently.

a) Work out the percentage contribution of
industry to the acid rain gases. Show your
working out.

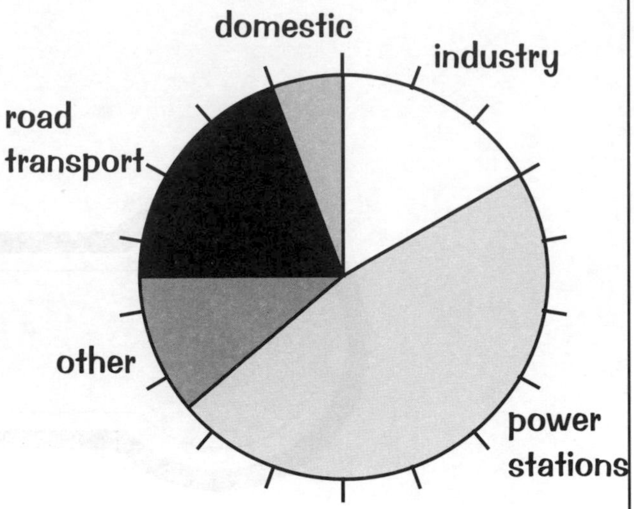

....

....

....

Percentage contribution = ... %

(2 marks)

b) Fossil fuels, such as oil, contain sulphur. Name the acid rain gas made when sulphur burns.

Name of acid rain gas ....
(1 mark)

c) Describe **two** effects of acid rain on the environment.

....

....

....

....
(2 marks)

8) a) Use words from the list below to write a word equation for respiration in the box.

water   **oxygen**   **carbon dioxide**   **glucose**   **energy**
(2 marks)

b) Give **two** uses of the energy released by respiration.

1 ....

2 ....
(2 marks)

SECTION SEVEN — TRIAL EXAM

9) The map below shows a farming area.

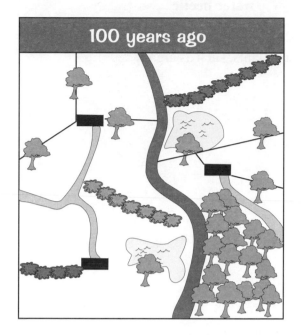

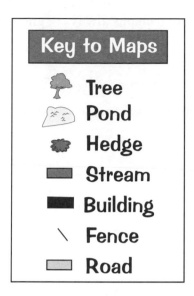

a) The farmer wants to make his fields bigger by removing the hedges.
   Describe the likely effects on the wild animals of doing this.

....

....

(2 marks)

b) The farmer wants to increase his yields by using insecticides on his crops.

   i) Explain what might happen to the wild animals on the farmland as a result of doing this.

   ....

   ....

   (2 marks)

   ii) Why might the insecticides harm the animals living in the river and ponds?

   ....

   (1 mark)

10) Study the food chain below. The biomass of each living organism is given under its name.

$$\textbf{algae} \quad \rightarrow \quad \textbf{daphnia} \quad \rightarrow \quad \textbf{water beetle}$$
$$\textbf{(100g)} \qquad \textbf{(60g)} \qquad\qquad \textbf{(10g)}$$

a) Why do food chains always begin with green plants, such as algae?

....
(1 mark)

b) Name **one** consumer in the food chain.

....
(1 mark)

c) What is the source of energy for almost all communities of living organisms?

....
(1 mark)

d) Draw a **pyramid of biomass** for this food chain in the space below.

(3 marks)

11) Study the food web on the right.

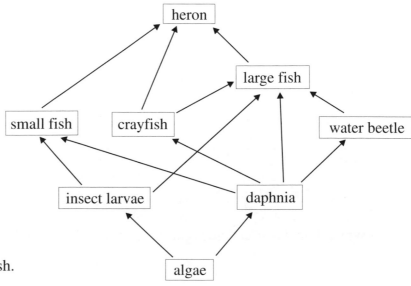

a) Name **two** prey of the large fish.

1 .... 2 ....
(2 marks)

b) Name **two** predators of the daphnia.

1 .... 2 ....
(2 marks)

SECTION SEVEN — TRIAL EXAM

c) i) Write down the longest food chain in the web.

....
(2 marks)

ii) In which direction does energy flow in this food chain?

....
(1 mark)

d) The insect larvae mature, and the insects fly away.
Explain what might happen to the population of daphnia as a result of this happening.

....

....
(2 marks)

12) a) Write down the types of microbe shown in the diagrams below.

i)

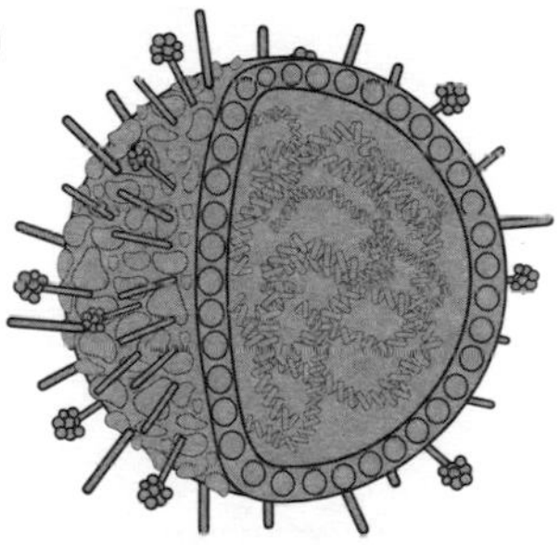

ii)

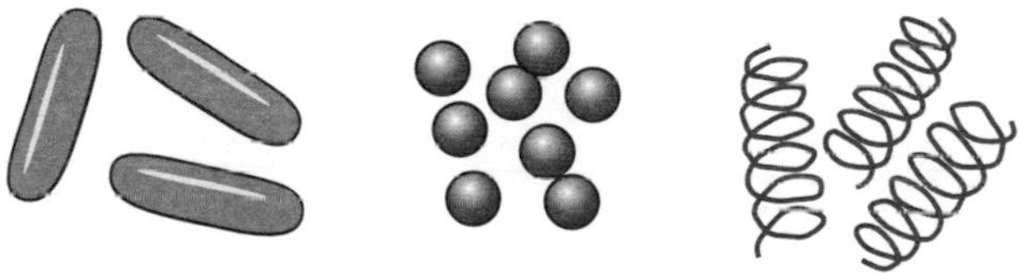

Microbe in i) ....
(1 mark)

Microbe in ii) ....
(1 mark)

b) Describe how the breathing organs defend against microbes getting into the body.

....

....
(2 marks)

c) Explain why we feel ill when harmful microbes enter the body.

....

....
(2 marks)

SECTION SEVEN — TRIAL EXAM

13) The picture shows a fossil of an ancient leaf.

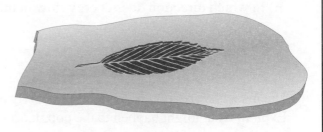

a) What can the study of fossils tell us about life on Earth?

....

....

(2 marks)

b) Describe how fossils can form.

....

....

....

(2 marks)

c) Fossils cannot tell us everything about the plants or animals from which they form. If you were making a dinosaur movie you would have to guess some things about the dinosaurs in the film. Suggest **two** important characteristics that you would have to make up.

....

....

....

(2 marks)

END OF EXAMINATION

1) a) Use words from the list below to complete the sentences about blood

white   red   pigment   oxygen   carbon dioxide   nucleus   cell   fluid

(6 marks)

The blood contains .... cells which transport ....

Red cells contain a .... called haemoglobin.

.... cells and platelets have no ....

White cells, red cells and platelets are carried in a .... called plasma.

b) The diagrams below show cross-sections through three types of blood vessels.
They are not drawn to scale.

A   B   C

Write down the names of each type of blood vessel.

Vessel **A** ....

Vessel **B** ....

Vessel **C** ....
(3 marks)

c) Explain how the white cells help to defend the body against harmful microbes.

....

....

....
(3 marks)

2) a) Give **two** examples of sense organs.
    For each sense organ, write down the stimulus to which it responds.

    Sense organ ....   Stimulus ....

    Sense organ ....   Stimulus ....
    (2 marks)

    b) Ashley touches a hot object with his finger. His finger quickly moves away from the heat.
    Explain how this happens.

    ....

    ....

    ....

    ....
    (3 marks)

    c) Write down a function of the spinal cord.

    Function ....
    (1 mark)

3) The diagram below shows a section through the human eye.

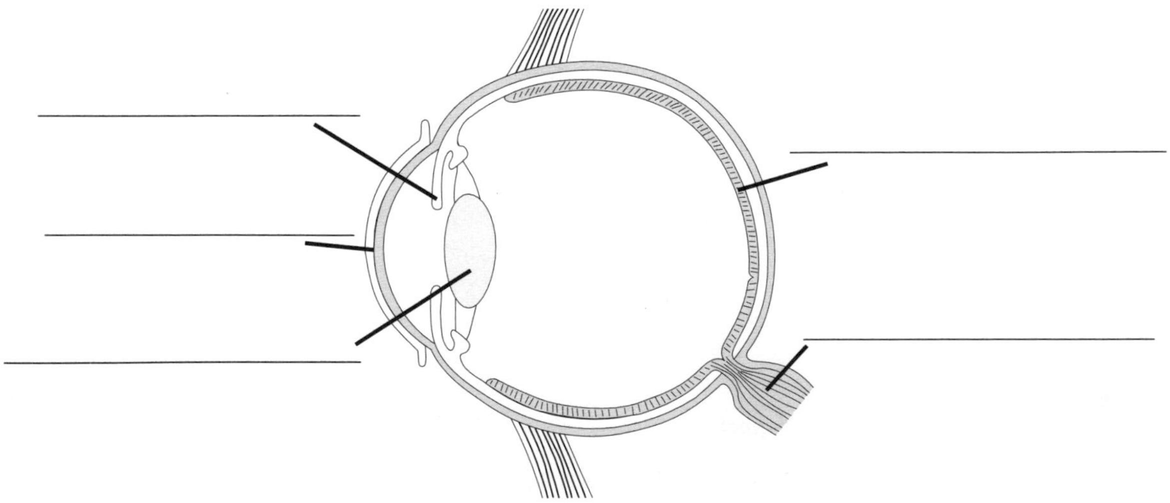

    a) Use words from the list below to label the parts of the eye.

    iris   lens   retina   optic nerve   cornea
    (5 marks)

b) Explain how the iris controls the amount of light entering the eye.

....

....

....

(3 marks)

c) What is the function of the lens?

....

(1 mark)

d) What is the function of the optic nerve?

....

(1 mark)

4) The picture shows a germinating seed. When a seed germinates, its root usually grows in one direction, and its shoot grows in the other direction.

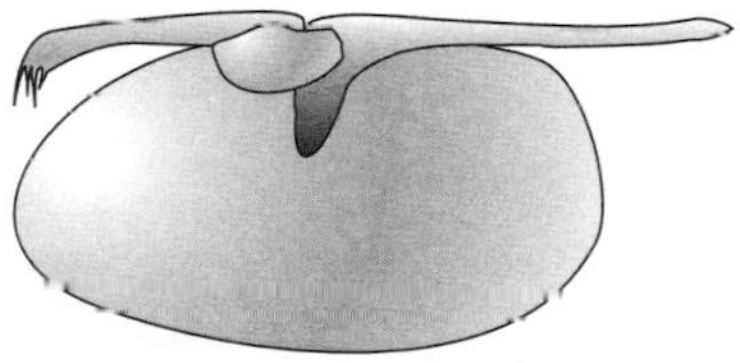

a) Name **one** stimulus that the growing shoot responds to.

Stimulus ....

(1 mark)

b) Name **one** stimulus, different to your answer to part a), that the growing root responds to.

Stimulus ....

(1 mark)

c) Describe the responses of the growing shoot and root to the stimuli named above.

....

....

(2 marks)

d) What type of substance controls growth and reproduction in plants?

....

(1 mark)

SECTION SEVEN — TRIAL EXAM

150

5) The picture on the right shows a
   flowering plant. Give **one** function
   of each of the following parts
   of a flowering plant:

a) Stem ....

   ....

b) Root ....

   ....

c) Leaf ....

   ....

(3 marks)

6) Gardeners often produce new plants by taking cuttings
   from older plants. The picture on the right shows how
   this can be done.

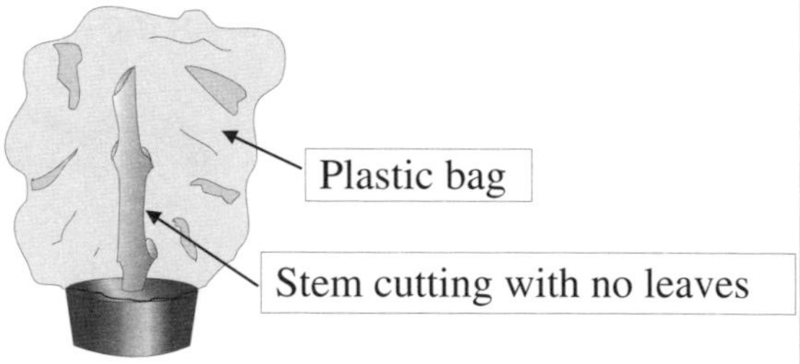

   a) Suggest why cuttings are likely to grow best when
      they are kept in a moist atmosphere until roots grow.

   Plastic bag

   Stem cutting with no leaves

   ....

   ....
   (2 marks)

   b) Give **one** advantage of producing new plants by taking cuttings.

   ....
   (1 mark)

   c) The new plants produced by taking cuttings are clones of the parent plant.

      i) What are clones? ....
      (1 mark)

      ii) What sort of reproduction produces clones? ....
      (1 mark)

7) The diagram on the right shows an experiment to investigate photosynthesis.

The plant was left in a dark cupboard for 24 hours to remove starch from the leaves, then it was exposed to light.

Leaf B

Leaf C (completely surrounded with foil)

Transparent glass jar

Leaf A

Sealant

Soda lime

a) What was the function of the soda lime? ....

(1 mark)

b) Why is the sugar produced in photosynthesis often converted into starch by the plant?

....

(1 mark)

c) After a while, starch was found in leaf B. Explain why no starch was found in leaf C.

....

(1 mark)

d) Would leaf A contain any starch at the end of the experiment? Explain your answer.

....

....

(2 marks)

e) Complete this word equation for photosynthesis:

.... + water + light energy $\rightarrow$ .... + glucose

(2 marks)

f) i) Name the green pigment found in plants, and explain its function.

....

....

(2 marks)

ii) Where in plant cells is the green pigment found? ....

(1 mark)

Lea
mar
bla

8) The diagram on the right shows a cell.

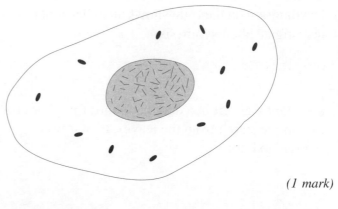

a) Write an **X** on the diagram to show where the genetic information of the cell is found.

(1 mark)

b) Use words from the list below to complete the sentences about genetic information.

chromosomes   **mutations**   **characteristics**   **genes**   **conditions**

The genetic information is carried by .... which are carried by the

.... in the cell. Different genes control different ....
(3 marks)

9) a) In humans, which sex chromosomes are found in males, and which are found in females?

Sex chromosomes in males .... Sex chromosomes in females ....
(2 marks)

b) i) What is the male sex cell (gamete) called, and where is it produced?

....
(2 marks)

ii) What is the female sex cell (gamete) called, and where is it produced?

....
(2 marks)

c) Complete the genetic diagram below to show the inheritance of gender in humans.
(5 marks)

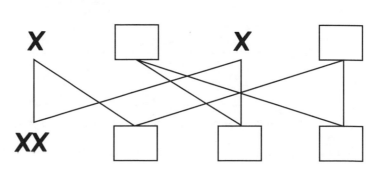

chromosomes in parents   **XX**   **XY**

chromosomes in gametes   **X**   **X**

chromosomes in offspring   **XX**

10) Hormones can control the monthly change in the thickness of the lining of a woman's womb and the release of an egg from her ovaries.

a) What is a hormone?

....

....
(3 marks)

b) Two hormones control the level of sugar in the blood. Name **one** of these hormones.

Name of hormone ....
(1 mark)

c) Waste products must be removed from our bodies to maintain health.
Name a waste product that must be removed, and briefly explain how it is removed.

....

....
(2 marks)

11) The graph below shows the changes in the number of birds in a wood.

a) What word is used to describe the number of a particular species in an area?

....
(1 mark)

b) i) In which year of the study was the number of birds the lowest?

Year ....
(1 mark)

ii) Give **two** possible reasons why the number of birds fell in this year.

1 ....

2 ....
(2 marks)

c) Suggest a reason why the number of birds never reaches very far above the number shown by the dotted line.

....
(1 mark)

SECTION SEVEN — TRIAL EXAM

d) When animals or plants die, natural processes can recycle the carbon in their bodies. Describe **two** processes that can return carbon to the atmosphere.

1 ....

2 ....

(2 marks)

12) Enzymes are biological catalysts. They are used by animals to assist many reactions needed to sustain life including the break-up of food in the gut. Different enzymes work on different reactions.

a) How is a reaction altered by the presence of an enzyme?

....

(1 mark)

b) Give the names of **two** enzymes used in the human gut and the type of food whose break up they assist.

....

....

....

(4 marks)

c) Enzymes are also used by moulds in causing food to go off. Fortunately, enzymes will only work under certain physical and chemical conditions. They are susceptible to changes in temperature and pH. Give an example of how each of these can be used in a food storage method.

....

....

....

(2 marks)

END OF EXAMINATION

SECTION SEVEN — TRIAL EXAM